ECHOES AND REFLECTIONS

Echoes and Reflections

KEITH A. WOOD

SERENDIPITY

First published in 2004 by
Serendipity
Suite 530
37 Store Street
Bloomsbury
London

British Library Cataloguing-in-Publication data
A catalogue record for this book is available from the British Library

ISBN 1-84394-100-7

Printed and bound by Alden Group, Oxford

Acknowledgements

I wish to thank Phyllis Campbell for getting the manuscript started and for typing the first chapter.

I am extremely grateful to Emma Fryer, not only for typing the greater part of the manuscript, but also for her continued advice and helpful suggestions for the layout and parts of the text.

I thank my daughter Judith for her many useful and critical contributions and for her valuable assistance with the proof reading. Also, thankyou to Sammy, Jo, and Roger of the Ipswich I Tec Services Ltd who have given me invaluable support.

The majority of this story has been put together from memory and I wish to apologise in advance for any mistakes I have made in names, dates and references. I am also very conscious of the omission of very many colleagues and friends who have helped to make my life so pleasant and interesting.

Finally, this book is dedicated to my wife, Dorrie, for her continual forbearance and support throughout.

Contents

Illustrations

Foreword by
Sir John Charnley

I first met Keith Wood in 1955 when I was posted to the Blind Landing Experimental Unit (BLEU) at Martlesham Heath in Suffolk. The Unit was a small multidisciplinary team of scientists and engineers tasked with the job of making it possible for aircraft to land safely in all weathers, fog in particular. Keith was the leader of the 'guidance group' and the impact on me of his positive, forthright views, enthusiasm, ingenuity and dedicated drive, backed by a thorough understanding of the relevant physics and electronics, was immediate. He 'nursed' me electronically so to speak for some time and I am privileged to offer some thoughts on these memoirs.

Many of the chapters read like extracts from a glossy brochure describing 'World Wide Adventure Tours escorted by K. A. Wood', but with the risks of many of his wartime exploits modestly dismissed. All chapters are 'peppered' with amusing anecdotes and lighthearted stories that make it encouragingly easy and rewarding to assimilate the more serious messages contained within them, so that with a little effort the significant technical achievements behind the exploits can be readily perceived.

Keith was born near Birmingham in 1915 but at the age of eighteen months his family moved to East Anglia in complete ignorance of the effect those bracing North East winds were to have on his character, career, and indeed his whole life. At times, he might appear to be a seasoned 'globetrotter' (more of that later), but the Deben estuary, Felixstowe Ferry and family circumstances were powerlul magnets always pulling him back to that locality. Happy childhood and school years are illustrated engagingly with accounts of farm animals and railway adventures, but the construction of a 'cat's whisker' radio at age ten and the selection of an aeroplane flight with some prize money at age thirteen, are perhaps early pointers to a future in aircraft electronic systems. Teenage training as a 'Sparks' provided worthwhile experience in radio engineering, but the real excitement started in 1935 when he was recruited by Robert Watson-Watt (later Sir Robert) to join the Airborne element of the new Air Ministry Research Station at Bawdsey (BRS) on the Suffolk coast as a Laboratory Assistant. The innovative excellence of the high powered scientists in this small team made a deep, lasting impression on the young Wood and fostered a strong career preference for a creative, energetic challenge in leading edge electronic research and development. This BRS model fashioned his professional attitude for almost seventy years and produced a success story well worth recounting.

Much has been written on the development of ground radar since those pioneering experiments of the mid thirties, but Keith's detailed and sometimes hair-raising accounts of the flight trials of the first ever airborne radar 'breadboards' and his later contribution to their development make enthralling reading, and add greatly to published knowledge. In 1941 he donned uniform in response to a call from the Royal Air Force to improve the performance of the radars in maritime aircraft stationed in Iceland, and this led to a personal invitation to visit the USA and assist with the development of Long Range Radar Aerials for their Catalina flying boats and for installation in Lend Lease aircraft due for delivery to the RAF. A twenty-one day Atlantic crossing, mainly in the superb elegance of a Boeing Clipper Flying Boat, was followed by a hectic five months zigzagging across North America, working hard in aviation centres but with cleverly arranged spectacular diversions.

Keith's next challenge began soon after the end of World War Two with a return to East Anglia to join the newly formed BLEU as leader of the guidance group and, as he remarks, 'complete with a sailing boat on a beach in front of my flat'. The first task was to explore a range of radio options for accurate flight path guidance to enable safe landings to be made in all weathers, at all times. A tall order, but attacked by the team with Keith's characteristic vigour, innovation and determination. In due course safe, fully automatic landings were demonstrated by BLEU and a blind landing capability, based partly on that early radio work, is now a standard fit in many commercial aircraft offering operational and economic advantages.

In 1957 BLEU moved to Bedford and Keith was recruited by the Atomic Weapon Research Establishment (AWRE) to take charge of their trials facility at Orfordness and so continued to live in Felixstowe. The creative atmosphere of AWRE, the encouragement of a like minded boss, and the isolation of the site suited him perfectly. As well as conducting nuclear weapon trials, with typical enthusiasm he devised 'home produced' aerials to track Russian Sputniks and monitor French nuclear activity in North Africa. This post was Keith Wood in his element and perhaps at his best. Incidentally it included a most exhilarating trip to Australia.

At age forty seven and after a brief, unhappy period in industry, Keith rejoined Government Service and was soon in London with responsibility for the technical administration of research and development in all civil aviation electronics, including his former interest of all-weather operation. He earned the respect of international experts at numerous world wide conferences but, of more significance perhaps, this post marked the beginning of regular commuting from Felixtowe to London, a pilgrimage he endured with undiminished enthusiasm and no loss of energy for another forty years.

Ten years later he made a second move to the private sector, this time for good. Eight fruitful years with Decca included a visit to Japan and was followed by a final twenty years, part time, in the technical secretariat of the Electronic Industry Trade Association, surviving four mergers along the way. Although not as challenging technically as earlier career posts, his wide experience and accumulated wisdom enabled him successfully to contribute to major projects in progress in the electronics industry.

The last chapter reflects upon two topics. The first is his deep appreciation for the tremendous support given by his wife Dorrie for her lifetime of dedication to Judith their disabled daughter, and here I would add my own tribute to Keith himself for the importance he always attached to family life when facing tough career decisions. Secondly, from his experience of research and development in both public and private sectors, he offers 'random thoughts' on a number of 'lively' topics which should not be missed. He in no way expects all to agree with his views, and I for one would take issue with some assertions, but as a stimulus to debate they are typical of his firmly held persuasions.

Echoes and Reflections is a fascinating tapestry of over seventy years of fulfillment, technical innovation and achievement, fluently narrated, and generously interwoven with amusing anecdotes and exciting adventures. I have found it a thoroughly enjoyable read and believe it should prove equally appealing to many others, both technical and not so technical.

Chapter 1

Early Recollections

I am very much an East Anglian at heart and particularly devoted to that part of Suffolk known as the Sandlings, of which, in recent times, a considerable area has been taken over by various 'green' organizations such as the National Trust, the Royal Society for the Protection of Birds, the Suffolk Wildlife Trust, etc. This very beautiful part of England is now known as the Heritage Coast.

My mother was a true East Anglian, born and brought up in the Station Hotel in Halesworth in Suffolk.

Birmingham

I was born in Birmingham but had the sense – or more likely the good fortune – at the age of eighteen months to leave that fine example of a city evolving out of the Industrial Revolution.

My father came from the Midlands, and I remember very little of him as he died when I was only eighteen months old. He was a victim of the great influenza epidemic which struck the whole country during 1918. I understand he held a position in the Accounts Department of the Dunlop Rubber Company in Birmingham. I believe he was quite handsome, and the marriage to my mother was quite the event of the year in Halesworth. Judging from my own assessment of my mother's character, I'm sure she entered into the marriage with enthusiasm and pride in 'capturing' her man, but with little regard to the responsibilities attached to such a contract. Not surprisingly the thirteen years they were together were turbulent and unhappy, to say the least.

My sister Muriel, or Woodie as she was known, was ten years older than I and it was from her that I learned what little I know of this period.

My first and only real memory of my father was painful. I was, I am told, just over eighteen months old when I displeased him during lunch one day and was made to stand in a corner whilst the others finished their meal. One can imagine the indignation suffered by the head of the family – especially in those days – by the blatant insubordination of my response. I can still remember every line of the green and gold pattern on the wallpaper which I had removed with the uttermost stealth. So much so that I had done a very considerable amount of damage before my industry was discovered. My father was furious, rightly, and I learned the hard way that rebellious satisfaction can be very short lived and can be paid for very dearly. I have remembered that subsequent thrashing with painful clarity. Perhaps it is unfortunate that this is the only clear memory that remains. This probably accounts, to some extent, for why I so much prefer the female of the species and why I have tended to be a 'loner' so far as any in-depth friendship with other males are concerned.

I have, of course, little knowledge of life in Birmingham except for what I have learned from an occasional chat with my sister much later on. Apparently the marriage was somewhat turbulent and my father, who was not strong in health, became a complete alcoholic.

The days in Birmingham were not very happy ones. My sister Muriel experienced this domestic situation for real, and looking back, her life seemed to have been made up of a number of different and difficult periods. Firstly in the ten years or so in Birmingham with a near alcoholic father and an unhappy and distressed mother. Then, towards the end of this period, the arrival of a very young and awkward little brother must have been very taxing. Later, in the Station Hotel at Halesworth as a teenager, working virtually as a chambermaid, dealing with the chores of the hotel and acting as a 'dog's body' to Aunt Edie, could not have been a very happy existence. Not surprisingly later, when she had given her early and middle years to being a breadwinner and devoted companion to our mother, she showed all the signs of one whose sacrifice had caused the years to slip away with little else to show for them. Woodie was always very kind to me and I like to think that the last years of her life were settled and contented. During that period she went to keep house in Weymouth for an old 'flame' that she had turned down years earlier because she had refused to leave my mother.

Returning to my very limited experience of life in Birmingham, I have another recollection even earlier during that period, which I have often used as an excuse to myself to explain my inability to deal with examinations or to tackle with any success such subjects as languages, history etc., which require, or are at least considerably assisted by, a good memory. Throughout my life my memory has been very selective and very dependant on an abnormal degree of interest in the subject or event concerned. At the tender age of eighteen months I fell from my cot by climbing over the top rail. I recall, just as a single 'take' so to speak, the very moment that I lost my balance, including the way in which the bedroom door seemed to start to turn over in front of me. I landed on my head and was unconscious for nearly a fortnight. My mother used to tell this story with all the minute detail including the final touch, which always intrigued me, "the first sign of consciousness returning was asking for a banana".

Another event in Birmingham will remain in my memory for life. I was taken to the city centre during Armistice celebrations to see the illuminated tram car. The sight of it was sheer magic and quite mind blowing. I can still recall in one 'take'- to use this photographic term again – a great deal of detail as this quite exceptional apparition passed from left to right as we were standing on its near side pavement. I also recall that there were so many coloured light bulbs in the total installation, generating so much heat, that the whole system had to be switched off frequently to avoid overheating.

Halesworth

On the death of my father in 1918 from the virulent influenza epidemic which hit most of Europe at the time, the three of us, mother, sister and I, went to live with my grandfather, Frederick Cowles, proprietor of the Station Hotel, in Halesworth.

Halesworth in those days was a very busy market town and the Station Hotel stood adjacent to the railway station on the Great Eastern line between Ipswich, Lowestoft and Great Yarmouth and on the main road to Bungay. Halesworth station was also the junction for Southwold, which was served by a small single line narrow gauge railway known formally as the Southwold Railway but in other circles by the less respectful but nevertheless endearing terms like 'Puff and Whistle' and 'Puffing Billy'.

The cattle market in those days was one of the largest in the district and on market days large numbers of animals passed to and from the market across the other side of the town just off the London Road. They were in transit from and to the trains which were the main means of transportation. Of course the farmers and the drovers used my grandfather's four ale bar to replenish their needs for refreshment after the day's exertions.

The running of the Station Hotel was a real family affair. My grandfather, Fredrick Cowles, was a rounded man of medium height, with an air of distinction about him. Rarely did I ever see him angry: it was beneath his dignity. He seemed to be able to maintain a poise in all aspects of a hotel proprietor's work whilst still being popular in the four ale bar. He was invariably friendly to all but had no favourites. My grandfather, as the head of the

4

family, was a well respected figure in the town and frequently served on the local council, being Chairman on occasions. I always remember the traumas throughout the household when he was caught by the local bobby with one or two farmers drinking after hours in the back smoking room. It was quite foreign to his image.

I learned a great deal from my grandfather, who always seemed conscious that I had no father to turn to. He always called me 'man', which was flattering, and he was always prepared to listen. He was an excellent gardener, and I have enjoyed gardening as a hobby throughout my life following his early tuition. Even later, when he became ill with cancer of the colon, he suffered largely in silence and with tremendous dignity. I thought a great deal of my grandfather and I missed him greatly when he died. His was my first experience of death at close quarters, so to speak, and I was overwhelmed not only by the loss but, I suspect, also by the lack of understanding of the full implication – which I still am.

During this period the family comprised my mother, sister and me, my Aunt Edie and her husband John Parker, my cousin Ivan and a cousin of my mother's named Flossie who was employed as a bar maid. It is not difficult to imagine the irritations which frequently arose, especially between my mother and her younger sister. Both were strong personalities but completely different in character. Aunt Edie managed the household and cooking whilst my mother assisted grandfather with the running of the hotel. My Uncle John had a position in management in the local Cobbolds brewery. Aunt Edie was a short rounded woman who displayed that general air of artificiality which one encounters in the so-called middle classes who are anxious to copy the local aristocracy. She could have quite a temper, but on the whole was a kindly person. She was over protective of Ivan, my cousin, who she claimed had a weak heart, and he only had to have a cold to be whisked off to bed for several days. She had unpredictable fits of emotion at times with which she seemed to taunt my uncle.

One favourite was to rush up the field opposite the hotel towards the 'big' pond, as it was known, with Uncle in pursuit in case she carried out her threat to throw herself in. This always seemed somewhat unlikely to me but it puzzled me that Uncle John, who was a big, heavily built man, should respond in such a timid manner to what appeared to be emotional blackmail.

As for my uncle, he was otherwise a somewhat severe character: a business man and a manager of the local brewery, who went to and from his nine to five job through the town twice a day looking neither to his right nor his left. A rather formidable character until one got to know him. I came to know him much better later on but was fascinated by his stories of experiences of the Boer War, including being blown across a small river in a freak wind storm.

Cousin Ivan was a lanky kid and generally speaking he and I got along very well, with the exception of the odd burst of irritation provoked by one or other of us. Unlike me, Ivan had a great interest in the military. Later, starting a career in the office of an Electricity Company, he became very active in the local territorial army. At the outbreak of war he joined the Forces proper and served much of the early war years in a special unit operating with the Sinusi tribes in the North African desert behind Rommel's lines. Referring back to his mother's concern about his heart, it is interesting to note that he became Middle East Army boxing champion, although I can't remember at what weight; probably middle weight.

The Station Hotel still stands and when last I heard it had become the local Labour Club. My grandfather, a staunch Conservative, would consider this a diabolical turn of events. The hotel was a pleasant building with a frontage covered in a very beautiful Virginia Creeper. For my cousin and me it had many other attractive features, not the least being a large yard on one side. Across the top of this yard were four stables, two of which housed very fine horses: one a beautiful chestnut and the other an equally beautiful black creature with a white flash on his nose. Along the opposite side was a large covered shed with open partitioned areas housing a small trap, an open carriage and a stately brougham, all of which were available for hire and did good business. The motor car had not yet arrived in Halesworth. This part of the business was completed with Joe the Ostler. Joe was a diminutive figure with the bandy legs of a man who had spent a greater part of his life with horses. I always marvelled how such a small man could have such command over two animals which towered over him. However, one sharp irritated snarl from Joe and they stood quiet as lambs. Joe also had a dreadful hacking cough which I suppose was a harbinger of the consumption which eventually killed him. His nose ran almost continuously and he was always wiping it with a very large red handkerchief with white spots. He also had a few very jagged teeth the colour of yellow ochre.

Soon after my arrival in Halesworth I found myself spending a great deal of my time with Joe in his harness room and around the stables and coach yard. I followed closely the feeding and grooming procedures and the harnessing and connecting of the different vehicles, the brougham, the trap and the open carriage. Although a little scared at first, I got to adore the horses. One of Joe's side jobs was regularly to clean the silver and cutlery for the whole establishment which he did grudgingly on a Friday morning. On occasion I would stand and watch him. Imagine the consternation at lunch one Sunday among the assembled diners – some eight members of the family and four visiting relatives – when in the middle of the meal someone remarked on the shining silver. Always anxious to demonstrate my newly acquired knowledge and in a burst of importance I announced how Joe always spat on the spoons, knives etc before applying the brimstone polishing powder. I was completely unprepared for the explosive reaction which my information triggered off. My Aunt Edie rapidly left the table to be sick and my uncle was given the task of tackling

Joe. After this I had the distinct impression that my presence in the harness room was no longer as welcome as it had been previously.

The very large yard with the hotel wall on one side, the coach sheds on the other, the stables across the top and a wall and gates across the bottom opening on to the road was of course a super playing area for us two boys. When I first arrived it seemed enormous and I could not kick a football the length of it. Several commercial travellers who regularly spent the night in the hotel would play a short game of football or cricket with us before setting out on their sales tour of the town and again sometimes before dinner in the evening. One in particular, who played regularly for some teams in Norfolk, taught us many of the finer points of these games. Also I had a number of friends among the farmers and drovers and often helped them drive their animals along the road and into the pens at the railway station yard. One such occasion provided an event which I have never forgotten. My cousin and I had been helping one of our farmer friends and his drover to drive a lively bunch of young calves that were being particularly difficult. As we neared the pens one lovely brown and white calf made yet another bolt for freedom, whereupon the farmer shouted "if you two boys catch him on your own he is yours". I shall never forget the resulting chase all around the station and across some allotments. We returned in triumph to the hotel yard and my grandfather, who had witnessed some of the scenes in the station yard and who had been tipped off by the farmer in the meantime, greeted us all smiles. He had already got Joe to put some clean straw in one of the spare stables and some milk in a bowl for Charlie, as we called our new acquisition. Charlie stayed with us for about two or three months but he began rapidly to outgrow us and the facilities. He was also very unpopular with Joe who found mucking out Charlie's stable very much more unpleasant than those of his beautiful horses. As a result, Joe's liberal vocabulary of expletives was markedly increased in frequency if not in content.

Another source of endless amusement for us boys was located at the back of the hotel between it and the maltings. Here was a small engineering workshop which, nowadays, would be termed agricultural engineers. Adjacent to the side of the corrugated iron building on a strip of waste land were two or three old broken-down traction engines, ploughs etc. In each case a number of the parts essential for a young boy's pleasure, such as the steering wheels, regulator levers and the like, still moved. We spent delightful hours here as make-believe engine drivers and invariably arrived home covered in a mixture of oil and rust to the dismay of our elders.

Of course the Halesworth railway station itself provided endless attractions. Firstly the platforms were split into two sections, being united, when trains were due, by a pair of massive platform gates which opened across the main Bungay road to form one continuous platform. Once one was 'well in' with the station porters there were opportunities for rides and I was always amazed how easily those massive structures were opened and closed by one man. The signal box too, at the south end of the platform, was a fascinating place but, for obvious reasons of safety, we were only allowed in this holy of holies on very special occasions.

I suppose the real highlight of our close relationship with the railway has to be the trains themselves. At around six o'clock every evening a goods train arrived from Lowestoft en route for Ipswich. This had to carry out shunting manoeuvres in order to add the wagons waiting in the Halesworth railway yards to those which had been collected at Lowestoft and the stations in between. The driver was a heavily built giant of a man called Smiler, for the obvious reason that he was a most jolly and kindly man. His fireman was named Paxman, Ted Paxman. Ted was, at that time, very keen on Flossy the barmaid, which turned out to be fortunate for me. I was continually pestering both him and Smiler for a ride on the engine, and I always thought it was to please Flossy more than me that I was invited to look over the engine one fine spring evening when to my delight I was allowed to remain on the footplate during the shunting operation, provided I remained seated in the corner.

This was the start of many absorbing trips over several months during which I, as a seven or eight year old, was allowed to make small contributions, such as stoking the boiler fire and sanding the wheels when they slipped. I remember the first time I was encouraged by Smiler to make the expedition out from the cab along the walkways round the engine attending to the many oiling and greasing points. The first few feet along the side of the cab where the walk was no more than a few inches wide was really scary and it took all my courage to negotiate this. After many such episodes I never really got used to this part of the oiling operations. Also, I never ceased to be scared of the operation of the safety valve, which often blew off a great geyser of steam without warning just above my head while I was attending to the oil cup closest to the engine cab. Smiler, who often caused it to happen, always got a real kick out of my discomfort!

The climax of this whole affair came when I was taken on the engine all the way to Ipswich one evening, where I stayed the night with Ted and his parents, and returned the next day using the same means of transport. Of course I had to be smuggled on to the engine and kept well in the corner of the cab with a sack over me whilst in the station at Ipswich and at those stations en route. This event made a very great impression on me and, I believe, gave me a first zest for the many new and uncertain situations which I encountered later in life. After all I had been part of an exciting plot to which I'm sure the railway authorities would have reacted very strongly had we been caught. In addition it involved sleeping away from home for the first time among total strangers, apart from Ted himself.

Incidentally I remember that in the morning, before returning to the Ipswich shunting yards, Ted took me to the Ancient House in Ipswich where he bought me a Tiger Tim's Annual and then to a toy shop where he bought me a train set. Later in this story you will read of other incidents in my life for which this railway connection at Halesworth was first class preparation for an adventurous spirit and taking on the unknown and uncertain. It is no surprise that my only ambition at the time, however, was to be an engine driver when I grew up.

The story of my link with the railway at Halesworth would not be complete without one more incident that, even now, makes my skin crawl with excitement when I consider the audacity of it. Beyond the railway gates on the Bungay road a lane went up an incline – almost a hill – on the right at the top of which was a large garden which also belonged to Grandfather. In it was a mixture of vegetables, soft fruit bushes and fruit trees and in the far corner a patch of grass facing south and west along the far fence. In this garden and just before the edge of the grass were the remains of one of the derelict coaches used in earlier days at the hotel. This, of course, became the ready made 'house' for us kids for a multitude of games.

Immediately beyond the fence a steep embankment covered in thick shrubs and bushes went down to within a few feet of the single rail of the narrow gauge Southwold Railway previously mentioned (Fig 1). On a particular summer afternoon my cousin and I had a friend playing in the garden with us. After exhausting our interest in all the usual facilities for our games we were engaged in 'cowboys and indians' among the bushes on the embankment when the train came up with its two carriages from Southwold. We watched the passengers disembark, followed by a stream of people joining the train for its return trip. I can't

1. Southwold Railway, Halesworth Station

remember which of us first suggested the idea, but we hit upon a plan to creep down to the railway under ample cover of the bushes and disengage the couplings between the two carriages. I should explain that the little station building, with porters and guards, was on the opposite side of the single track. This uncoupling was quite possible for boys of seven or eight years since everything was on a much smaller scale than normally associated with larger main railway equipment. With our hearts thumping, one of us kept 'cavey' whilst the other two disconnected the coupling between the two carriages, and we all crept back into the cover of the bushes to await events. After what seemed an age, the whistle blew and the green lamp was waved, as was the custom in those days. To our great delight away went the small engine with its one carriage whilst the other remained stationary, to the dismay of its passengers. There was a lot of shouting and 'hollering', as they used to say locally, and the train halted within sight and was brought back to be reconnected with its apparently reluctant carriage. I don't think any one of the officials was able to account for what had occurred. Certainly the runaway train incident was all round the town in no time and caused many a laugh in the four ale bar at the Station Hotel. We boys retreated up the bank under cover of the bushes and kept our secret!

About two years after arrival in Halesworth I should have started school, but it was decided to await two events, namely the opening of a brand new school just off the Wissett Road, which was expected within two years and the departure of my cousin for prep school at Southwold. Thus, in order not to get into trouble with the education authorities when we became of school age, my cousin and I were taught by my sister the basics of reading, sums, painting etc. She had a few problems at times with discipline but her efforts were not in vain.

Just before the school building was finished and Ivan had already departed for Eversley House in Southwold, I was fortunate to be befriended by two plumbers working on the new school. I was again scared but got used to climbing up and down the ladders whilst working on the large flat roof, which at the age of five was quite an adventure in itself. Plumbing in those days consisted of joining pipes by building up large amounts of solder into tapered elongated shapes around and on each side of the joint, and wiping it into its final shining rather elegant shape with thick wads of old rags. One soon learned to be wary of the small globules of boiling solder after only one or two painful experiences. One afternoon on arrival at the site, I climbed the ladder to look for my plumber friends on the massive roof, when imagine my excitement on finding in the corner of a chimney a beautiful straw nest with four large brown and white spotted eggs. When I found the two men at the other end of the roof I made their day with my excitement and was sent home later to inform everybody that I had found a stork's nest. Of course, later, what would have been an obvious leg pull to adults was revealed in the bar as the joke it was, and the eggs had been specially painted chickens' eggs. I have to confess feeling a bit 'let down', so to speak, but it was a useful lesson in the process of growing up and in not taking everything at face value or believing all one is told without question, even by friends.

When the school was completed, I was one of its first pupils and remained there until I was nine years old. Those were days of restriction, with incentives to make absolutely maximum use of the now much shorter period in the day for doing 'one's own thing', such as fishing in the 'big pond', damming the brook running down the Holton Road and playing with the children of the local butcher in their large garden. However this took second place to the tremendous interest in all aspects of Broadway Farm on the Bungay Road. Here I was always welcomed by the farmer and his wife, Mr and Mrs Lawn, and did my best to help with all the many jobs which occurred with the passing seasons. I had first hand experience of haymaking, driving tractors, feeding and mucking out the animals, and finding the eggs which some wayward hens laid all around the farm in hedges, hay and straw stacks etc ...

Later, in my late teens when I was working at the Bawdsey Research Station, I spent a delightful holiday with them. One of my most lasting impressions of that holiday was being put into a 20-acre field of sugar beet with a hoe in my hand and told to get rid of the weeds between the rows! One look across the field convinced me of Willie Lawn's advice not to look any further than the next few feet of the row in front of you. This experience taught one to get on and do the job properly and not worry too much about finishing, which will happen eventually. Useful philosophy.

Stowmarket

After the death of my grandfather and at the age of nine years I spent a short period living together with my mother and sister and with my Uncle John and Aunt Edith in their very nice regency house next door to the Hotel in Halesworth, before we moved to Stowmarket. My mother decided to use the money left her by my grandfather to set up what would now be called a boutique, and Stowmarket was chosen on the advice of some of the commercial travellers who had become friends of my mother over several years. I am sure the advice was good, since Stowmarket was a thriving market town, but the failure of the business some six years later was due to my mother's lack of real business experience and understanding. Her sense of clothes, of style and of fashion were very well developed and the shop was well located in the market square, but all her customers became friends for whom she made large reductions – she had little business sense.

Settled in Stowmarket, I was successful in obtaining a place in the local mixed grammar school which, on reflection, was a first class example of the grammar schools at that time. The Headmaster, whose name was Eldridge, was a tall fine man who always wore a stiff white collar and black tie. He was always to be seen at school in his academic gown and sash. He naturally commanded respect of staff and scholars alike and performance and discipline were generally at a high level. Of his staff, his deputy, the English mistress, was Welsh – Miss Bowden. Of the others I remember particularly, Mr 'Stumpy' Davies for gym and sport, Miss Todd, the ageing but very hard working French teacher, and Miss Ham who was gym and games mistress for the girls and also took geography. Miss Ham was certainly an attraction for all the boys as she hurried around the school in a very short gymslip with large shapely legs in black stockings which did justice to her name. I also remember a Mr Palmer who took music and made the subject so interesting that I have benefited from his efforts throughout my life from a listener's point of view. He took us through all the movements of Beethoven's Fifth Symphony, Handel's Water Music, etc ... The only other member of the staff I remember clearly was Mr Philips, the maths master, who also was master of the local Scout troup which I joined, and more of this later. I was never an outstanding pupil, although I did consistently well for Miss Bowden at English and for Mr Davis at sports, particularly cricket and football.

During this period I developed a very strong friendship with the son, Percy, and the daughters, Phyllis, Gwen, Jean and Pauline, of the local butcher, Frank Godbold and his wife. Behind his shop in the high street there was a very large yard, a number of buildings and beyond them a sizeable garden which gave scope for a variety of games and activities. Not surprisingly this combination, plus the ever tolerant Mr and Mrs Godbold, attracted quite a large gathering of friends of both sexes. It became known as the 'Godbold Yard Gang' which was always into some fairly harmless mischief. I remember on one occasion several boys with pea shooters lined up along the slab in the shop front on a Sunday evening as the worshippers came out of the Congregational Church across the road. As with many such shops in those days it was important to keep them well ventilated, so the top section of the removable shop front was in the form of a grille, and just right for shooting peas across the road with little chance of detection. It is easy to imagine the confusion that reigned when the joint peashooters unloaded their ammunition into this comparatively large mass of people. Of course, we were careful not to carry on after the first few bursts to avoid detection and to be safe, therefore, to enjoy this exciting game on other occasions. Another fairly harmless game we indulged in on a Saturday evening was to walk past a gathering of girls walking along the pavement of the crowded high street with a piece of thread stretched between two of us at about thigh level and watch the results!

Stowmarket had, at that time, a spartan council swimming pool in the river, and it was here I learned to swim. I eventually 'did' my mile in a temperature of 56° and I shudder to think about it even now.

Another family of friends were the Beavers of Tothill Farm just north of the town along the Bury Road. There were eleven daughters ranging from about 14 to 26. I had a particular early crush on Ena, a beautiful brunette of about twenty years. Sitting cuddled on her lap at the age of 9 was at that time my idea of bliss.

My first introduction to flying was quite unique and well worth recording. Whilst still at school in Stowmarket at the age of thirteen I took part in the town carnival, which was always a very splendid affair and fully supported by all the traders and the towns folk alike. I wore a very colourful rig supplied as an advertisement for a fly and insect spray product named 'FLIT'. The day was full of excitement and culminated in me being awarded the second prize of ten shillings and sixpence [in old money] in the under-fourteens class. This was a fortune to me in the days when the weekly pocket money for most kids of my age was only twopence. I remember thinking long and hard about how I should spend it, at a time when I was being urged by my mother to put it in the savings bank.

Finally I made up my mind in secrecy. One Saturday afternoon a week or two later, without the knowledge or the consent of my mother – who I knew would never have agreed – I took the bus to Ipswich and presented myself at the flight office at Ipswich Airport, which was a large grass field with one or two unpretentious wooden huts and a small hangar. On the grass in front of the buildings were two or three small biplanes.

With all the audacity in the world this young kid entered the flight office in which two or three men were chatting and asked

2. First Flight: Robertson Redwing

how much it would cost to have a flight. A tall dark young man eventually turned to me and said "a lot of money – how much have you got son?" My reply of ten shillings and sixpence caused them all to burst out laughing, and there were several jocular remarks about the price of aviation fuel and the cost of maintaining aeroplanes, during which time my heart sank lower and lower at the thought that my lofty ambition was rapidly coming to naught. However to my absolute delight the man who had first spoken to me, who turned out to be the instructor, declared that he was about to make a short test flight in the Redwing and "I'll be damned if I won't take him with me". There was some cautionary discussion about insurance and about taking minors, but my 'hero' had made up his mind, and handing me a helmet, led me out to the aircraft. I have since discovered that the Robertson Redwing was a biplane with a 75hp Armstrong engine especially built for training (Fig 2). It was a smart little aircraft and one of the first to be designed to have side-by-side seating, which allowed very easy contact and communication between instructor and pupil. I was soon settled in beside the pilot. With all checks completed, a man on the ground swung the propeller, the engine immediately roared into life, we taxied to the downwind edge of the airfield, and with a thrilling roar we were off. Never before or since have I felt such a mind-blowing sense of elation and intense excitement as we soared over the trees and the whole vista of Ipswich and the River Orwell opened before us.

The day was ideal as, in brilliant sunshine, we flew over the river towards the estuary and the sea at about two thousand feet. By this time I had just about got my breath back when my pilot began to demonstrate the various controls. I was even allowed to hold the control and make small banking manoeuvres.

We flew out to sea from the mouth of the Orwell for about two miles then turned to the east and proceeded parallel to the coast, past the entrance to the River Deben as far as Orford and the river Alde. At this point we turned round and headed back down the coast, flying very low along the Shingle Street bank – what a thrill that was – and on reaching the Deben estuary did a climbing turn inland to Ipswich airport where we landed. So ended one of the most wonderful events of my life. I handed over my ten shilling and sixpenny postal order in the flight office to much laughter from the same three men and with many thanks, departed. Unfortunately I never did know the name of my pilot hero.

Of course when I got home I was still so excited that I blurted out the whole adventure and my mother was furious, but when she calmed down I believe she was quite proud of me.

Little did I realize how this flight and particularly the very route we had taken along this part of the Suffolk coast would feature in my career both at Bawdsey and Martlesham Heath, flying on Radar experiments in the late 1930s [see Chapter 3] and at Martlesham Heath and Woodbridge Flying on Blind Landing research and development in the 1950s [see Chapter 6].

My experience over several years with the Scouts, including camping, helped develop relationships with many other boys of different characters, and our favourite camping site was at Haughly Park between Stowmarket and Bury St Edmunds, where we learned the basics of cooking and a great deal about nature and the countryside. During my time in the Scout movement I was fortunate to attend a World Jamboree, which took place in Arrow Park in Birkenhead near Liverpool. I met scouts from all over the world and struck up a friendship with a Norwegian. The following year he invited me to a Norwegian National Jamboree held on the edge of the Hardanger Fjord. The scenery was quite mind-blowing and such a contrast to East Anglia and anything I had experienced previously. The organized treks in the mountains behind the fjord were memorable for the grandest of scenery and were quite exhausting. Scouting, as I knew it, was educational and character building. A great movement for young boys.

As I have said before, my mother was always up to date in her outlook, and whilst at Stowmarket invested in a three valve radio 'receiver'. I spent many an hour 'wandering around Europe' playing with this new 'toy' and I quickly built up a general interest in radio and the basis on which it worked. Mother had purchased it from the local jeweller who had a shop just across the road, and he was the local amateur. He encouraged my interest and under his guidance, at the age of 10, I built a crystal set. Imagine my excitement on hearing London 2LO transmission but, looking back, the fiddly business of making a contact with the 'cat's whisker' could be very irritating. However, this growing interest in radio was to be an impelling force on my choice of career later. Indeed, one incident related to Mother's radio set provided a clear indication that a career in radio was inbred, so to speak. In those early days of radio as an entertainment service it was normal to have to change the batteries regularly, both the high tension 150 Volts and the low tension 2 Volts which supplied the valve filaments. When the first change became necessary my mother got the various connecting leads mixed up and put the high tension 150 volts on to the valve filaments and bust all three valves. When the jeweller was called, because the set would not work, he declared that all the valves were in fact, burnt out, and he replaced them. My mother could not understand how this could be and moved the offending connector on to the terminal as before with the remark "All I did was this". In those days it was a costly action and six valves cost a lot of money. Clearly her son was destined for a career in radio!

At Stowarket at the age of 13 I first drove a motor car at over 60 miles an hour; quite illegal of course. It was a friend's MG Midget on the road between Haughley and Stowmarket, and I saw my first 'talkie' film *Broadway Melody* about this time.

The years at Stowmarket taught me a great deal in many ways. I had my first teenage sweethearts. Firstly an attractive dark haired girl named Mary Phillippo and then Jean Godbold. The latter was a lovely fair haired girl with a very kind nature. Jean was my big heart throb well into my twenties. I learned, from my mother's problems with the shop and her eventual bankruptcy, about the seriousness and misery of bills and debts. This latter situation brought the first realization that I had to take a more serious view of life and prepare to earn my own living.

Chapter 2

Starting a Career

At the age of fifteen I, and those around me, realized I would not benefit greatly by staying on for higher school. Meanwhile, I had been building up a strong desire to become a Radio Officer (a Sparks!) in the Mercantile Marine. This grew from my early interest in radio, a certain attraction to the uniform and the possibility of glamour if posted to a cruise liner. In the event, my mother and my uncle agreed to me using the money left to me by my grandfather to pay for one year's tuition at a school for radio operators in order to obtain the necessary PMG certificate. I chose the Wireless College at Colwyn Bay in North Wales and soon after my fifteenth birthday I joined this establishment for the autumn term in 1930.

The year I spent in Colwyn Bay was an education in more senses than one. I had little difficulty with the work which consisted of basic electrical and electronic theory, a basic understanding of radio transmission and reception and a working knowledge of and the ability to operate the Morse Code and the associated radio transmission and receiving equipment.

The College was owned by an ex-Radio Officer, one Mr Whale, and he had two assistants, both also ex Mercantile Marine. Apart from the radio apparatus the facilities were very basic and there were few comforts. The management took the line that this was deliberate in order to prepare one for the rigours of some of the smaller and less well equipped ships in the merchant navy and fishing fleets.

The fellow students were a very mixed bunch with a distinct

majority of Irish. I became friendly with a very well-mannered and intelligent chap named Brambleby but it was otherwise prudent to keep one's own council as it took little to spark off a fight. Colwyn Bay was a pleasant town with a nice pier. The college was on a hill and steps went down to the promenade level, which included a bridge over a brook called the Dingle running down to the sea. This stream was running between walls of stone blocks and was some three to four feet across. I remember Brambleby, who was quite athletic, would invariably jump across from wall to wall rather than use the bridge. Several of us were challenged to do the same and many got a good soaking and some nasty bruises to show for it!

Apart from work there was little of significance during the three terms. I was quite homesick and could not wait for the end of term and holidays with friends in Stowmarket. I left in the July of 1931 with a 1st Class PMG Certificate.

After the year at Colwyn Bay, and at the age of seventeen, I was faced with my first big disappointment. A world recession meant that the chances of obtaining a position as a Radio Officer in the Merchant Navy were zero for all practical purposes – many experienced licensed officers were having to take shore jobs in radio factories, having lost their ships which were being laid up in increasing numbers. It was this realization and the need to have more experience of radio that led me to apply for a short term apprenticeship (2½ years) with a company in Bedford named the Igranic Electric Company. This was a subsidiary of the American Cutler Hammer Group manufacturing electrical switch gear. The company was in the process of developing a radio arm to its activities and it was this branch of the company to which I applied and was accepted with formal arrangements to spend periods in each of the main departments, including assembly, winding room, drawing office, testing and research/development.

For the first year or so I had 'digs' with a widow and daughter who were known to the Godbolds in Stowmarket. Percy Godbold, their son, had also taken up an apprenticeship with this same company. Later my mother and sister decided to move into a house in Bedford so that we could be together. Bedford had a nice river and we all enjoyed punting and picnics. I liked the work and seemed to progress well but, of course, the wages were minimal and there was little one could afford to invest in spare time pursuits. I took part with some fellow apprentices in the occasional Saturday evening skirmishes with Oswald Mosley's 'Black Shirts', for whom we all had a particular dislike. However I have never enjoyed belligerent activities and soon found myself using my time more usefully with night classes. I also joined the Bedfordshire Yeomanry as a territorial. This at least provided me with an opportunity to learn to ride a horse. The name escapes me, but the riding master, a regular army Sergeant Major, was a character who got more than his fair share of sadistic pleasure from the multitude of mistakes his raw charges made. He had a 'contract' with the horses which persuaded them at his special communication to throw the rider, who would then be greeted with "Who the hell told you to dismount?" The unfortunate recipient of his little joke would start to scramble back on the horse only to be greeted with "Who the hell gave the order to mount?" Only to have the unfortunate chap virtually suspended in mid air not knowing what to do.

My last assignment with Igranic was in the Research and Development department and, looking back, it provided the first evidence of a latent urge to continually seek the new rather than the routine. This was to be a cornerstone of my driving incentive through life. My two and a half years at the Igranic was concluded with good relations on both sides and I was made an offer to stay on in the R & D department at a nominal salary for the time. However, I wanted to try something new now that I was over twenty years and I applied for and secured a post in the Factory Test Department at A C Cossor, in the Highbury district of London, at considerably more money than had been offered at the Igranic. The experience was useful and interesting initially but the hours were awkward in that one had to be in the factory one hour before all the other workers in order to carry out the calibration of the routine test equipments on the production lines before the factory test engineers arrived at eight a.m.

After a few months I left to go first to E. K. Cole at Southend and then to EMI at Hayes to take up a job in the Test Equipment Development Department. I managed to find digs close to the factory, which I shared with a factory test engineer, Ronald Cooper, who was destined to take the same path as I in the coming months.

I was still somewhat dissatisfied with my type of work which, although not as boring as the factory test, was nevertheless only just a little more interesting and less tied to the bench, so to speak. At this point, looking back, I embarked on an 'intuitive action' which was to change my life in so many important ways. I saw an advertisement in the *East Anglian Daily Times* for a post of Laboratory Assistant in a new research unit being set up on the coast in East Anglia. The words 'Research' and 'East Anglian Coast' were an immediate trigger and I applied.

In late 1935 I was called to an interview in the old Adastral House, Kingsway and I spent about one hour being questioned by the Chairman, Robert Watson-Watt (Later Sir Robert), A B Jones and J Airey. I met Jones and Airey later, the former as the Administrator and the latter as Head of the Model Shop at what turned out to be Bawdsey Research Station (BRS). The job sounded very mysterious and intriguing but, of course, any attempt to prise more details from members of the Board failed. It appeared that the work would be connected with radio direction finding and sited at a new research station at Bawdsey in Suffolk. The down side was that it carried a salary of only twenty nine shillings and sixpence per week in old money compared to five pounds a week, which I was earning at EMI.

My uncle, with whom I discussed the proposition, was a manager at Ind Coope's Brewery in Romford at the time and a typical business man. He was appalled that I should even consider it. "You never go backwards, my boy" he said and I am sure his advice was well meant in my interest. However, in retrospect, if I had taken his advice I am sure it would have been the worst decision I could have made since, in accepting, I opened up a new style of life and received an unexpected second education from some of the finest scientists in the country – more of that later.

I took the job, gave notice of one month at EMI and planned to move to East Anglia in the vicinity of Felixstowe which I had known well from school days. An early visit to Felixstowe in preparation for going to Bawdsey was successful in obtaining 'digs' with a rather unusual couple, Mr & Mrs Layborne, in what was then the Coastguard Bungalows in the small fishing village two miles north east of Felixstowe called Felixstowe Ferry. These bungalows were destroyed by a bomb from a Dornier dive bomber during the war. Immediately across the River Deben was the Bawdsey Manor Estate, which had been acquired by the Air Ministry and was known as the Air Ministry Research Station Bawdsey (BRS).

Chapter 3

A Bawdsey Boffin

Arriving from Felixstowe Station I little realized then how very much the small fishing village of Felixstowe Ferry would endear itself to me and become so much a part of my life as it still is now some seventy years later.

The Laybornes were a couple whose life had been in service as cook and butler for many years but they had recently set up in the Coastguard Bungalows with the intention of taking summer visitors. This unforeseen opportunity to have several young men stay during the winter months was a pleasant surprise, although we were warned that we could not stay after the week before Easter. However we all welcomed the opportunity to get to know the locality before making other arrangements.

The others were young men who had also taken appointments as laboratory assistants at BRS and who wished to be comfortable and close to the job, only two minutes walk to the ferry over the River Deben. The Laybornes had a small snooker table which offered some leisure activity, and the bungalow was adjacent to the end of the local golf course, its front facing the sea only some two hundred yards away beyond the sea wall. Behind was more golf course and then the marshes stretching to the north for miles inland along the south shore of the river Deben. The perfect setting for those wonderful East Anglian sunsets for which this part of the country is famous. The Ferry, as it is known locally, consisted of an assortment of wooden huts and comparatively modest houses, and it has not changed very much since. The population of some one hundred souls were occupied in fishing, running the two pubs – the very ancient Ferry Boat and the more recent Victoria – and a bus service to Felixstowe. Others worked down in the town some two miles to the south. There was also a thriving boat building business run by men who were very skilled in the construction of wooden boats of all kinds. The boss was Pop Pearce.

Amongst the locals were a number of quite wonderful characters including Ernie Aldous who was proprietor of the Ferry Boat and Vic Keeble who ran the Victoria. Ernie was an abnormally big man with a squeaky falsetto voice who was at his best when pontificating on the topic of the day. Albert, who was Ernie's son, was a phlegmatic character with a slow, deliberate manner. He was always on the right side of anything involving money! These two ran a bus service between the Ferry and the centre of Felixstowe. Two buses were used, both very second hand from, I believe, the Eastern Counties Bus Company. Obviously they passed the requirements of the Ministry of Transport but were in pretty poor shape inside. Later I was told that an incident involving BRS was recorded in the log book. The story related how Albert was driving past the Golf House which was about half way to Felixstowe when the bus broke down with engine trouble. Albert went into the Golf House, borrowed a phone and called his father who came with the other bus to tow Albert back to the Ferry. Surprise, surprise – this was too much for the second bus which promptly broke down also – whereupon Albert, recalling all the stories he had heard about 'death rays', returned to the Golf House phone again, rang up the Administrator at BRS and his words were "will you turn that bloody thing orf over there oi can't get either of my buses to goo".

Another character was Skipper Dan with a very long white 'Father Christmas' beard. The more discerning stood to windward of Dan when listening to his most interesting tales of his earlier experiences on the oceans. He was not noted for changing his clothes very often!

3. Jockey Hunt

4. Skipper Bryant

5 Charley Brinkley

There were several Newsons, including Tommy, Josh, Gager, Settler, Sailor and Connie, and a wonderful character called Jockey Hunt (Fig 3) – I'm sure I've left some out. Then there was Skipper Bryant (Fig 4) who lived in a derelict boat, the *Whisper*, moored in the mud by the river bank. I have a very amusing story about Skipper Bryant which will be more appropriate later. All these were very real individuals and wonderful characters. There are now few left and that is a great pity.

There was also an artist who lived in a slightly more acceptable hut called 'The Studio' with his son and daughter. He was nicknamed Corkie as he had a false cork leg. Corkie's daughter Erica was attractive and turned out to be a great favourite with all the young men at the Research Station. Her brother was a gangly lad who often got involved in somewhat amazing activities. For example, he had a very old BSA motor bike with the round tank. He would ride full throttle down the slipway into the river and then spend the next few weeks taking it down, desalinating it and greasing it only to make a repeat performance when he began to get bored.

In those early days we were taken over the Deben by boat rowed by one Charlie Brinkley senior (Fig 5). Charlie was in his late seventies and he had a hook for a hand lost in his youth. The hook was designed to just fit in the hand grip of a standard oar. The boat would take four or five passengers and with the currents which run in the Deben estuary, particularly during the period of spring tides, this was quite a feat of strength and long experience. Later the Air Ministry provided Charlie with a motorboat and a small jetty on each side which was safer, quicker and could cope better with the increasing numbers, as more people joined BRS from Felixstowe and district.

Charley was no respecter of senior people and made no distinctions. On one occasion I remember one of our Senior Officers, who did not normally travel across on the ferry, insisted on standing up in the stem of the boat. After one or two requests to sit down, Charley, much to the amusement of us juniors, yelled in a stentorian Suffolk voice "Will that silly bugger standing up in the stem sit down or he'll get hulled out". Whilst still on the subject of the ferry operation it is worth mentioning the story of Charlie's compass. He had been given a compass to help with the crossing on dark nights and in November fogs. When the first opportunity came to use it on a very thick evening in November we finished up way down the opposite bank by several hundred yards. An examination later exposed the fact that the alcohol in which the magnet had floated had provided a pick-me-up for one of his pals earlier and what little remained was such as to lead to a very erratic performance. The fact that the compass was mounted on top of the engine didn't help the situation either.

It is not difficult to imagine what an interesting experience it was to become involved in this small community, especially since there were already scary stories around about this new research activity over the water where they were "almost certainly developing Death Rays"!!

Another important development for me, personally, was that it was here in Felixstowe Ferry that I leant to sail a dinghy. My instructor was a local young man, Brian White, who was later to become a colleague at BRS. On leaving school, he joined BRS as an assistant and became a very valuable and well known member of the airborne radar team. I owe Brian a great deal, not the least the many years of very pleasurable sailing both in racing dinghies and later in a very high performance day boat of Swedish origin called a Vitting. I gave up this activity at the age of eighty three when I no longer had the agility and sense of balance required to enjoy it.

Throughout the remainder of this book Felixstowe Ferry will feature again and again in my life in many memorable ways.

Having settled in my new quarters in the Coastguard Bungalows

6. Bawdsey Manor

I set out on a blustery wet day in late November 1935 and arrived at the Bawdsey quay having been rowed over the river Deben by Charlie Brinkley Senior – the ancient mariner mentioned earlier with a hook for his left hand. An Air Ministry police officer escorted me up the long winding drive to the Bawdsey Manor house (Fig

6) and into the office of the Administrator, the Mr A B Jones of the original interview in London. After the formalities he told me I had been allocated to the newly formed Airborne team. After various formalities I presented myself to the leader of that team, Dr E G Bowen (known to all as Eddie or Taffy), in their laboratories at the top floor of the White Tower. There were five others in the team, namely Dr A G Touch (Gerald), Robert Hanbury-Brown (known by all as Hanbury), Bill Eastwood, Perce Hibberd and Sidney Jefferson. I made up the total of seven and the team stayed at this level until the spring of 1937 when two more were added – R Mills, and B D W White.

Soon after I arrived, Eddie Bowen gathered the five of us together to discuss his plans for the work on airborne radar. Finally, to illustrate the size of our task he took us up to the main Ground to Air radar transmitter site to see the early prototype pulse transmitting and receiving equipments. "There," he said, pointing to a large hut full of equipment, 'is about two tons of equipment and all we have to do is to get it into an aeroplane!' There were no miniature components in those days so the task seemed daunting.

Before describing the aims and the work of the Airborne team in detail it may assist understanding if I describe the real intentions behind the setting up by the Air Ministry of the Bawdsey Research Station and its objectives. It all started in 1934 when the Government circulated several research units confirming their concern about the large build up of German bomber aircraft and the threat they posed. The circular was seeking ideas for disrupting the ignition systems of aircraft engines as a possible counter. Robert Watson-Watt (later Sir Robert) at the Radio Research Station at Slough had a team measuring the movement of the ionized layers above the earth upon which some important communication services depend. These measurements were made using very short pulsed high frequency radio transmissions directed up at the layers

7. Airborne Radar Team

and timing their reflected return. He did some calculations and reported that some significant levels of radio energy could be reflected from aircraft and returned to the origin where it could be received and the time taken would indicate the range. He was given a small sum of money to mount a trial to demonstrate this. A receiver was set up at Weedon in the vicinity of the BBC Daventry HF Radio Station and an RAF Heyford aircraft was flown towards and around it. When the aircraft was within a few miles the direct signal received suffered rapid amplitude fluctuations which were not present without the aircraft thus indicating interference by the reflected energy. This was known as the Weedon experiment, named after the place where the receiver was sited.

This result stimulated expectations and further support from the Air Ministry. As a result, more money was made available for a proper experiment at Orford Ness in Suffolk using one of the pulse transmitters from Slough suitably modified. At the time I joined Bawdsey Research Station (BRS) return signals or echoes were being received from a Scapa Flying Boat flying 17 miles out to sea off Bawdsey using a developed pulse transmitter/receiver on about 10 metres wavelength using special dipole aerials mounted on 240ft wooden masts. This main ground system for the detection of aircraft in the air was known as RDF1 (Radio Direction Finding) and this was selected as a deceptive code to camouflage the real intent. RDF at that time was a radio navigation aid and well known worldwide. It was the Americans who later named this technology RADAR, and this new title has stood the test of time. Our intention in the airborne team was to use radar in an aircraft to detect ships and other aircraft in the air.

A simple Definition of Radar

A Radar system is a special form of radio in which the transmitter and the receiver are located in the same place and both often use the same aerial. In Radar the transmitter starts the operation by launching very small packets of energy of very short duration called pulses. In between each transmitted pulse the receiver is active and collects any small packets of energy which may be reflected from objects which are within the field of view of the aerial. The transmitted and received pulses travel out and back at approximately the speed of light. Near object reflected energy arrives comparatively quickly and that from objects further away takes longer. Thus the lapsed time between the transmitted pulse and those pulses received from objects such as ships, aircraft, buildings etc., can be measured. Light travels 186,000 miles in one second or 328 yards in each millionth of a second and therefore is a direct measurement of the range to each object from which a reflected pulse is received. For example the pulse received from an object approximately 1000 yards away will be received 6 millionth of a second after the transmitted pulse taking into account that it has to travel out to the object and back again.

In practice the radar measurement of range is usually combined with conventional methods of direction finding to provide the full indication of the position of the object in either two or three dimensions.

Knowing the time taken for the energy to travel out and return the distance to the aircraft could be determined based approximately on the speed of light.

At this point I must make it clear that the main purpose for setting up BRS was to press on with all speed with the Ground to Air detection (RDF1) programme, and a large team was deployed on this work. The Airborne Radar was just a small project to look at the feasibility of such an operation and the job was given to a very small team of six people under Dr Bowen – of which, luckily, I was one. (Fig 7)

The airborne radar program was given the code RDF2. The first decision we had to make was the frequency to use, and this had to be dictated by the size of any reasonably acceptable antenna that could be fitted externally on an aircraft. It was decided to use a wavelength around 1.5 metres and Gerald Touch and I were given the task of building a suitable special receiver 'breadboard' on this wavelength. Fortunately Watson-Watt, who was now the Superintendent of BRS, had used his influence to 'steal' an EMI 45 Mcs tuned radio frequency (TRF) amplifier which was being planned for receiving the first BBC television transmissions. We planned to use this as our intermediate frequency (IF) stage of a special receiver. The radio frequency (RF) amplifier and oscillator stages were built around the new Acorn valves that had just been made available. During the first weeks of 1937 the 'breadboard' prototype began to take shape, including a Cossor Cathode Ray Tube (CRT) display. This had a horizontal timebase giving an amplitude/range display 100 microseconds or 10 radar miles long because the original signal is reflected and therefore when received has travelled twice the time and therefore twice the distance.

Meanwhile our transmitter team had not been so successful and had failed to find a valve that could produce any worthwhile power at 1.5 metres. Retuning and synchronizing to a powerful 7-metre ground pulse transmitter, using Naval NT36 valves 'thrown together' in the White Tower, this breadboard detected the Trimley Water Tower at four miles from the top of the Red Tower of the Manor using a half wavelength dipole and reflector aerial. Incidentally this signal from the water tower exactly four miles away became our standard test before going to Martlesham airfield to fly any new equipment. At this point Eddie decided to put this air/ground arrangement into practice in an aircraft and this combination became known as RDF 1.5 with the transmitter on the ground and the receiving equipment in the air. In other words half way to a full RDF2 airborne system and hence RDF 1.5. The 7-metre pulse transmitter which had been quickly assembled in a corner of the White Tower laboratory fed an aerial which was

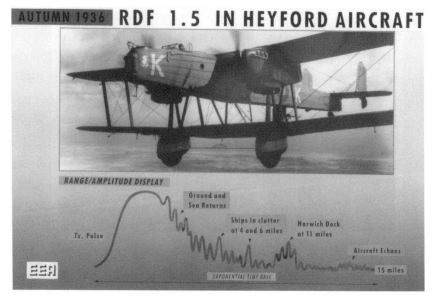

AUTUMN 1936 RDF 1.5 IN HEYFORD AIRCRAFT

RANGE/AMPLITUDE DISPLAY

Ground and Sea Returns

Ships in clutter at 4 and 6 miles

Harwich Dock at 11 miles

Tx. Pulse

Aircraft Echoes

15 miles

EXPONENTIAL TIME BASE

8. RDF1.5 in Heyford, 1937

rigged on the roof. I remember that the 10k supply to the anodes of the high power transmitter valves was slide back wire. When the resident cat walked under it its hair all stood up on end. Health and safety officers would have had a fit!

Arrangements were made with the Aircraft Experimental Establishment at Martlesham Heath to use a Heyford bomber aircraft for this first experiment (Fig 8). A 7-metre half wavelength loaded dipole was slung between the spats of the fixed undercarriage for the receiving aerial. The RF, IF and display time base circuits, all with their power supplies, were mounted on a wooden board and placed on the small navigator's table. The display CRT was slung above on spongy rubber from the aircraft framework and provided with a black photographer's cloth for viewing. After some problems with ignition interference from the Rolls Royce Kestrel engines – quickly dealt with by their Resident Engineer – we made our first flight. Hanbury and I flew out to sea over Felixstowe for about ten miles and were having great difficulty maintaining synchronism with the ground transmitter. However, when the timebase held occasionally as we turned towards the land we were thrilled to see the sea returns and spikes of pulses from buildings and one or two particularly strong ones which we suspected were coming from St John's Church spire and from the large crane used for lifting the flying boats from the water at the Marine Aircraft Experimental Establishment. After this flight we flew several times with improved synchronization and confirmed our results.

In the meantime our colleagues had had success with their hunt for a valve which would produce some power at 1.5 metres. A 316A 'Door Knob' made in America was able to produce sufficient power on 1.5 metres if overrun well beyond its continuous wave (CW) rating. This was not as bad as it seems since we were using small 3 microsecond pulses at 1000cps; even so each valve did not last very long!

The team set up a receiver/transmitter on the White Tower using suitable half wave dipole aerials and acceptable echoes were received from the Water Tower. At Martlesham two 1.5 metre dipole aerials were slung under the wing of the Heyford and the transmitter breadboard was placed on the floor with its attendant 120 high tension (HT) battery, 2 V accumulator and vibrator extra high tension (EHT) supply. Hanbury and I flew out over Felixstowe as before and were delighted to get much the same results as with the RDF 1.5 equipment, but now this was full RDF 2. In addition to the sea and ground returns we also saw some moving echoes coming from around the airfield at Martlesham which we thought were probably from aircraft. Thus a full transmit / receive pulse radar was operating in a Heyford aircraft in flight in the early spring of 1937.

This was a World First!

Once again the very encouraging results of RDF 1.5 and RDF 2

AUGUST 1937 RDF2 IN THE ANSON AIRCRAFT 6260

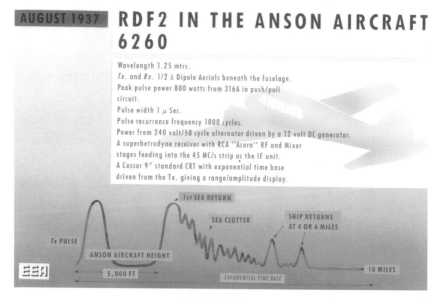

Wavelength 1.25 mtrs.
Tx. and Rx. 1/2 λ Dipole Aerials beneath the fuselage.
Peak pulse power 800 watts from 316A in push/pull circuit.
Pulse width 1 μ Sec.
Pulse recurrence frequency 1000 cycles.
Power from 240 volt/50 cycle alternator driven by a 12 volt DC generator.
A superhetrodyne receiver with RCA "Acorn" RF and Mixer stages feeding into the 45 MC/s strip as the IF unit.
A Cossor 9" standard CRT with exponential time base driven from the Tx. giving a range/amplitude display.

1st SEA RETURN
SEA CLUTTER
SHIP RETURNS AT 4 OR 6 MILES
Tx PULSE
ANSON AIRCRAFT HEIGHT
5,000 FT
10 MILES
EXPONENTIAL TIME BASE

9. RDF2 in Anson

in the Heyford produced even more excitement at the Air Ministry and consequently more support. This time the support came in the form of detaching from 220 Coastal Squadron, Bircham Newton, one of the newest and fastest aircraft in Coastal Command, namely the Avro Anson. This was one of the first operational monoplanes in the air force with two Armstrong Siddeley Cheetah engines. Since this one, number 6260, did not have its rear gun turret fitted it probably was one of the fastest aircraft in the RAF at the time.

We immediately set about equipping this aircraft with an ASV (Air to Surface Vessel) radar installation. After much trial and error on the ground we fitted it with horizontal transmitter and receiver aerials and we replaced the 120V HT batteries and the glass jar accumulators with an engine driven alternator designed and made for us by the Electrical Engineering Department at RAE Farnborough. We also installed a pen recorder.

By the end of August this aircraft was producing very good

results varying between 3 and 4 miles in tests over the North Sea using as targets the various ships plying between Harwich and the Continent (Fig 9). One, in particular, which we named the 'Danish Egg Boat' provided a useful standard target since it operated a regular service and we could always plan to use it as necessary. Now occurred a very important initiative on the part of Eddie Bowen. He got a friend in the Air Ministry to alert him to plans for a RN Fleet Exercise in the North Sea involving RAF Coastal Command aircraft early in September. We planned to have Anson 6260 on top line for this opportunity and at dawn on 4 September 1937 we took off from Martlesham Heath at 05.15 and headed out into the North Sea. The visibility was very bad and we could not see across the airfield. We were Dr Bowen, Sgt Pilot Naish and myself. We were fortunate to have Naish with us since not only was he an excellent pilot but he was also an ex-Merchant Navy officer and an expert navigator. Visibility was fine above about 500 feet but below that it was very thick. We did catch a glimpse of the Sunk lightship on the way out which had been showing on the radar about 4 miles before we reached it – a useful check that our equipment was performing normally. After about 40 minutes flying at about 10,000 feet we began to see several small echoes coming into the maximum range (10 miles) of the time base. Flying towards these to our great joy into the end of the display time base at 10 miles came what to us was a huge echo many times bigger than we had ever seen before. It came from the *Courageous* aircraft carrier and to complete the picture, a number of smaller echoes indicating her destroyer escorts.

What a sight, and what a repayment for all the efforts of the small dedicated airborne team in so short a time. Figure 10 shows an annotated picture traced from the CRT display during this exercise with the fleet. Interpolation based on the amplitude of the pulse from the *Courageous* when it first came on to the time base

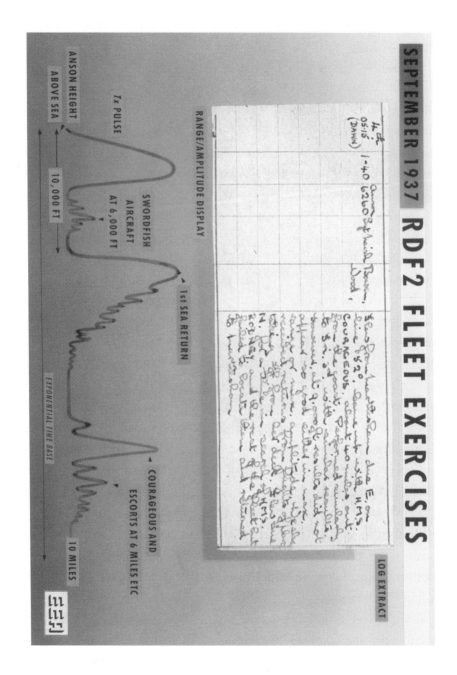

10. RDF2 Fleet Exercises

at 10 miles indicated that we would have seen it coming out of noise at more than 20 miles had we had a longer time base.

However, this was not all of the outcome of this momentous flight. Suddenly, several small but very distinct echoes appeared between the original transmitted pulse and the first and main pulse return from the sea directly below us. Moments later Sgt Naish reported several Navy Swordfish aircraft had come up through the fog layer and were making up and towards us. They had been dispatched to see what lone aircraft was flying around and over their ships. This then was the first real air to air pulse radar contact and under almost true operational conditions.

Another World First!

Having acquired some excellent records of this complete operation we turned for home under even poorer visibility than earlier. Sgt Naish's navigation was as good as ever and we saw on the radar at 4 miles the Sunk lightship again and flew over it, thus obtaining an excellent fix. A little later we picked up the big 240ft radar masts at Bawdsey and we also had the radar pulse indicating the nearest coastline and other outstanding features inland. At this point we descended into the murk to about 300 feet over the water exactly beside Bawdsey Manor and straight into the mouth of the Deben River (Fig 11). We had flown up and down the Deben so often that following its bends until we came to Martlesham Creek was negotiated with comparative ease in spite of the very poor visibility. Here as usual we 'turned left' and proceeded to descend along the normal approach path to land safely on the grass airfield. A quite incredible flight from start to finish. On arrival Eddie Bowen phoned the Air Ministry Operations office and made a verbal report of the position of the *Courageous* and of the several escorts. He also gave the number and formation of Naval Swordfish intercepting aircraft. To say that the man was surprised is to put it mildly –

11. The Deben Estuary

he was quite speechless. His first words were "you do know the RAF Coastal Command Exercise was cancelled very early this morning and all the aircraft had orders to remain on the ground because the very poor visibility would have made an exercise unsafe?" Of course our Anson on experimental flying was not part of Coastal Command exercises. The fact that radar could enable it to operate in such weather was not generally known at the time.

The reader needs little prompting to imagine the overall effect this flight in Anson 6260 on 4 September 1937 had on all those involved both in the Services, both Airforce and Navy, and in the Government Departments concerned with BRS administration and its programmes.

One result was to provide Eddie with several new staff and we were joined by Ralph Mills, Brian White and later John Grey. Another very tangible result was a rapid decision to equip this small airborne team of scientists with facilities to carry on our further research and development simultaneously on both ASV (Air to Surface Vessel) and on AI (Air to Air Interception). Thus,

44

12. 'D' Flight, Martlesham, 1938

in a very short time our Anson was joined by another and
then two Fairey Battles, a Harrow, a Hampden and a Magister
communication aircraft. In addition we were allocated the large
bomber hangar at Martlesham and a complete flight of pilots
and all other supporting trades to maintain the aircraft and
to provide assistance to the scientific team. This became known
as 'D' Flight under a commanding officer, one Sqd Ldr Butter
(Fig 12).

From early 1938 to early 1939 the work involved developing
our ASV equipment further and improving its performance,
adapting it for use in the air interception role (AI) and investigating
many types of aerial and their performance in different positions
on the various aircraft. Before starting this general aerial work
Touch and I set about developing measuring equipment and
procedures. This involved feeding a signal into the aerial under
test and moving round it at a constant distance with a receiving
aerial feeding into either a sensitive thermocouple or a small valve

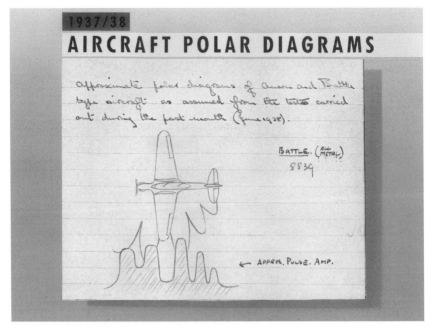

13. Airborne Aircraft Polar Diagrams

receiver depending on the task. These readings were plotted on polar graph paper to illustrate the coverage.

This work was to prove most valuable later when designing radar in new types of aircraft both in UK and in the assignments I would be involved in overseas. As part of this programme our air crews worked out flight plans which allowed us to plot rough polar diagrams (Fig 13) in the air in both the horizontal and vertical planes. This involved one Battle aircraft flying around the other in both the horizontal and the vertical planes at a constant distance in a controlled manoeuvre requiring considerable flying skill. Such flight tests established that the ground measurements were broadly maintained when airborne. They were also used to indicate the best direction from which to approach aircraft in order to obtain the maximum detection range. Since almost all aircraft have a nose, a tail and one or two wings on either side, the generality of this result made it very useful. An Anson has a similar pattern to the Battle, for instance.

I have pointed out before what little knowledge or respect we had for aerodynamics. At an early stage in our search for the most efficient aerial on an aircraft Gerald Touch and I were in the Anson over the sea at about 5,000 feet. We had a 1½ metre horizontal dipole aerial on each wing mounted in front of the leading edge; one for transmission and one for reception. In the middle of this sortie we were checking our signal against the 'Danish Egg Boat' as usual when Gerald had an idea. Considering the basic sea wave structure was mainly horizontal he thought the performance might improve if the dipole aerials were to be vertical instead of horizontal as the interference from reflections from the sea would be decreased. Without hesitation he asked the pilot if, on the next run up to the target, he could turn the aircraft through 90° so that the horizontal dipoles on the wings would be vertical. With a cheeky grin the pilot acknowledged the request and just as we settled on the next approach he turned the aircraft up on its side, so to speak, and struggled to keep it there for what seemed a long time but was probably a few split seconds and then reverted to normal flight. Immediately I turned to Gerald with the excited question 'well, how did it go? – what result did you get?' Looking distinctly shaken the answer I got was 'Christ! I forgot to look in the tube!'. We landed and promptly planned to put both vertical and horizontal dipoles on the aircraft for the next flight test.

The next aerial programme was, perhaps, even more incredible and arose from the three priority tasks, namely, ASV, AI and a new concept called Long Range ASV (LRASV). The latter requirement was based on the idea of efficiently sweeping the surface of the sea on each side of the aircraft for targets so that the tedious and time consuming traditional square search would be unnecessary. The requirement was to produce an aerial which would have a comparatively narrow beam 'looking' out sideways at right angles to the normal line of flight. We produced several

THE FLYING WASHING LINE

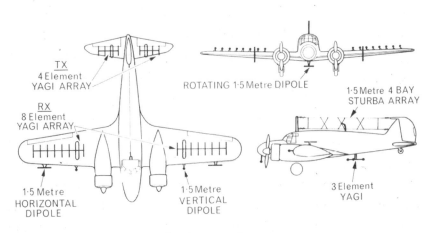

ANSON 6260
1·5 Metre R.D.F.
1937

TX
4 Element
YAGI ARRAY

RX
8 Element
YAGI ARRAY

ROTATING 1·5 Metre DIPOLE

1·5 Metre 4 BAY
STURBA ARRAY

1·5 Metre
HORIZONTAL
DIPOLE

1·5 Metre
VERTICAL
DIPOLE

3 Element
YAGI

14. The Flying Washing Line!

possibilities including a Yagi array, a Sterba broadside array and an array of horizontal dipoles. During the period we also investigated several other aerials including aerials above and below the wings to form overlapping beams in the vertical plane and on either side of the nose for similar overlapping beams in the horizontal plane. We also had a 1.5 metre dipole which could rotate fitted under the nose section. I am almost ashamed to say that at one stage Anson 6260 had examples of all these aerials installed together and being flight tested. The readers with any knowledge of aerodynamics will be appalled! They will also not be surprised that the aircraft could hardly take off. We were essentially scientists and radio engineers and had the audacity to put 16 dipole Yagi receiving arrays on the top of each side of the main plane and another two 4 dipole arrays on the top surface on both sides of the tail plane. No wonder 6260 was, at that time, known as the 'Flying Washing Line' and could only just stagger into the air (Fig 14). It is to be noted that, after the war, I received a

Gratuitous Award to Inventors from the Government for my airborne radar aerial developments.

The considerable database which was built up about the behaviour of various types of aerial configurations and their performance in relation to various parts of the aircraft fuselage was to be invaluable when, later, I was faced with fitting ASV and LRASV into new types of aircraft both in the UK and abroad. We also developed a variety of impedance matching devices for the efficient transfer of the signal from the feeders to the aerials.

During this period this small team also found the effort to investigate one or two other uses for airborne radar. A flight was made at a constant height across the UK from East Anglia to Lancashire, over the Pennine Range, using the radar as an altimeter measuring the ground range directly beneath the aircraft. This was compared to the heights shown on an Ordnance Survey map. After one or two flights it was evident that radar could provide an excellent 'height above ground' altimeter and could be used as an important aid to navigation in future which heralded the possibility of the famous H2S equipment.

Another operational possibility was conceived and a number of flight tests made on a project we called 'Bombing From Above'. In this system it was assumed that the German bombers would attack in large numbers closely formatted for protection against fighter attack. The scheme was to have an aircraft above the stream which would be able to 'see' the aircraft below on the radar. A bomb would be dropped, in the tail of which would be a small radio receiver. The falling bomb would show an echo on the radar as it descended, and when its echo beat with the echoes of the raiding aircraft below, a transmitter in the aircraft would send out a signal and detonate the bomb. Using the two Battle aircraft we took this equipment to a point where it appeared to be entirely practical. We received excellent pulses returned from the falling bomb following a series of drops using different lengths of copper wire to cause the bomb to resonate at the frequency being used. One of these flights was nearly a disaster. The wires attached to the bomb were folded and secured by a very light string whilst in the external bomb rack. The string was supposed to break on release and the wire stream out. On this particular occasion, with a long wire, the string broke on take-off with the bomb still in the rack. The long wire got entwined around one of the ailerons and the several minutes involved in completing the take off, circling and landing with a partially jammed aileron called for great flying skill, especially with a Battle aircraft, which was built like a battleship and was very heavy. That, for me, was a happy landing!

I seem to remember it was sometime in the summer of 1939 that Winston Churchill visited BRS and Martlesham Heath. He was still a backbencher at the time but well aware of the gathering storm. At the airfield he was shown the AI in one of the Blenheims and insisted on getting into the seat to see the indicator for himself. He went to a lot of inconvenience to achieve this. Back at BRS later he, of course, saw the ground-to-air radar – a forerunner of the radar chain stations of which several hundred were completed during the war all round the UK. Later in the day we explained 'Bombing From Above' to him and on the roof of one of the new buildings he was to watch the smoke bomb with a receiver in its tail blown up from the transmitter when he pressed the red knob. It did not explode and a laboratory assistant was seen out in the field crawling towards the bomb platform to investigate. He had covered only half the distance when it suddenly exploded. Winston's immediate reaction was that everything he had seen during the day had behaved perfectly and now he knew it was all genuine!

Yet another operational possibility was to use LRASV to produce the silhouette of a ship through cloud for identification purposes. Using the comparatively narrow beam 'looking' out sideways from the aircraft and flying at about 500 feet about two miles away

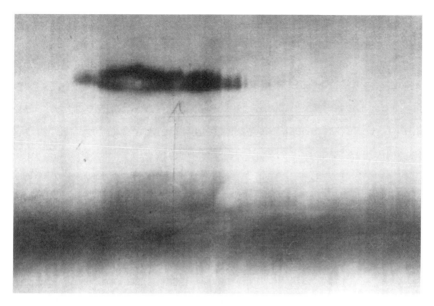

15. Courageous 1.5m Radar Image

and on a parallel path, a pen recording of an aircraft carrier was obtained (Fig 15). This indicated clearly the possibilities for the future, particularly if higher frequency transmissions became available with increased definition. Another early indicator towards H2S type possibilities.

We also slung a 14' cathode ray tube on elastic in the entrance to the bomb aimers compartment in the nose of the Anson beside the pilot. No other protection! A rotating time base fed with radar signals from a rotating dipole provided an early Plan Position Indicator (PPI). The picture was crude and lacking in definition but the potential was obvious and our other aircraft flying around us as targets were seen very approximately in the correct relationship on the 360° time base.

All these activities in research and development were brought to an end in June 1939 when war was thought to be almost inevitable. All the limited effort available was switched to development for production of both ASV, LRASV and AI. This meant liaison with companies in the radio industry such as EMI, Murphy Radio, Metropolitan Vickers, Pye Radio and EK Cole etc. Three new long nosed Blenheim night-fighter aircraft with four Browning guns in a pod underneath were delivered to Martlesham Heath and our small research team, with the help of the engineering facilities at Martlesham and at BRS, set about equipping them with AI, MkI and this occupied us all into September.

Again during this period we experienced the first of the team to be lost in an aircraft accident. Grey had joined us as a laboratory assistant during the recruiting effort in mid 1939 and was involved in a test of IFF radar (Identification Friend or Foe) in a Scapa flying boat. The Scapa was an aircraft with a very high reliability and safety record. However, as it flew along the coast at 1000 feet about a mile or so off Felixstowe it quite suddenly dived almost vertically into the sea. Grey and all on board were killed. A week or so later I attended his funeral at Tow Law in Durham on behalf of BRS. A sad experience. Imagine my reaction when at the weekend I was in the Ferry Boat Inn when Ernie Aldous, in his piping voice, announced "O' course it stands to reason that they had to make sure the bloody thing worked at least once for real!"

At about this time Eddie Bowen and I had quite a scare on one occasion during flight testing one of these night-fighter Blenheims. We were at 10,000 feet over mid-Suffolk when the aircraft began to fill with smoke. These Blenheims were the long nose variety and we had installed our AI Mk 1 equipment in the nose which we had screened off with a fitted sheet of five plywood. It was soon obvious that the source of the smoke was in the nose compartment. Eddie was beside the pilot, Sgt Pilot Argent, in the front and I was behind with receiving equipment in the rear section behind the main spar. Eddie grabbed a hatchet from its retainer on the side of the fuselage and broke into the nose section and then emptied a fire extinguisher into it, having first removed the mains supply to the MK 1 equipment. By this time the air was very thick with acrid fumes. The source of the trouble was the mains transformer which had developed shorted turns. Fire in the air is very scary and is doubly dangerous because there are always strong draughts to fan any flames. Fortunately in this case there were no flames. Sgt Argent was quite wonderful. There was no panic and he appeared to ignore the situation and continued to fly the aircraft back to Martlesham Heath quite coolly in spite of the, by now, very thick smoke, leaving Eddie and me to deal with the source of the trouble.

Meanwhile it would be wrong not to write a short section describing a little more of the environment of BRS and Felixstowe Ferry during this period. I have mentioned already the winter of 1937 in the Coastguard Bungalows. During this time I acquired my first car for £5 in old money. It was a square nosed Morris Oxford Coupé. Fig 16 shows it outside the Coastguard Bungalows. When the holiday season arrived and I had to vacate the Layborne's guest house I managed to hire a small houseboat, *Japonica*, moored in the mud at the Deben riverside at Felixstowe Ferry (Fig 17). She is still there and used for summer holidays. A little primitive, but good fun in the summer. I obtained digs in Felixstowe when the autumn came along and as I said before, I continued to enjoy sailing with Brian White and what I learned brought me much pleasure for years to come. The thrill of a racing dinghy planing with the bow wave up at shoulder level lives in one's memory.

During this period, Gerald Touch was very interested in nature and, particularly, in ornithology. At one stage I got caught up with one or two amusing experiments which he planned. He was intrigued with the ability of homing pigeons to find their way back to their own loft from a distance. He arranged to borrow a couple of birds from a friendly farmer and pigeon fancier in mid Suffolk, some 30 miles away. On some occasions we let them go at BRS

16. First Car: Morris Oxford Coupé

17. *Japonica* houseboat

when the big radar pulse transmitters were off and at other times when they were transmitting on full power. There were indications that in the latter case the birds seemed to take longer circling around before setting off for home. However, there was not sufficient clear evidence for him to report to the RSPB. Nevertheless they were always back in mid Suffolk before we could get there in Dr Bowen's Riley sports car. On one even more amusing occasion we collected the birds and kept them turning in a small cage on an old fashioned gramophone turntable in the back of the car with me keeping it wound up. They were then released many miles away. This we did several times but the birds always got back quicker than we could by car!

Other diversions from the work were visits to my friends the Godbolds at Stowmarket with a bank clerk friend David Adams who had lodgings in the same house in Felixstowe and had an early Ford Popular motor car. It was in 1938 that I first met the girl who was to become my wife. Dorothy [Dorrie] Pinner was a local Felixstowe girl who joined BRS at that time as a stenographer and we met first crossing the Deben on the way to work in the Bawdsey Manor. For the next twelve months the war situation ensured that we had a difficult time meeting since she went to various locations with the main radar team of BRS whereas I, with the airborne team, was destined to be on airfields elsewhere. We eventually came together and married in Farnborough in 1941, of which more later.

Meanwhile, the potential for war was increasing week by week and on 3 September, 1939 everything changed. All the BRS staff and their equipment left the Bawdsey Research Station for Scotland and Dundee University. The station then began its operational role as RAF Bawdsey and one of the vital links in the radar detection chain of stations on the East Coast.

Chapter 4

Early Airborne Radar at War (1939–43)

War is Declared

Just prior to the famous – or infamous – 3 September 1939, we in the Airborne Team at Bawdsey were working hard at Martlesham Heath to complete the installation of Air Interception Radar (1½ metre AI Mk1) in three Blenheim night-fighter aircraft which had already been fitted with four Browning machine guns in a pod under the belly of the aircraft between the wheels of the undercarriage. The radar installations had been completed and the aircraft were due to be delivered that very day to 106 Auxiliary Squadron (City of London), made up of volunteers from city banks, insurance brokers and stock market companies. This squadron was based on the airfield at Northolt, west of London. As planned, Hanbury Brown, a Flight Sergeant, whose name I can't recall, and I set off at 0900 hrs on this delivery flight. The assignment was to include some initial training for those who would be operating the equipment on normal squadron interception operations.

After arrival we were standing on the tarmac getting to know members of the squadron when at 11.00 a.m. the Prime Minister, Neville Chamberlain, made the announcement on the radio that we were at war with Germany. I remember the buzz that went round the squadron at this announcement and the sudden activity to prepare for whatever was to be expected from the much vaunted German bomber force.

In discussions with the Squadron Commander, who was I believe the Viscount Carlos, it was agreed that the three Blenheim night-fighter aircraft must be prepared for German raids that night. Since there had been so little time for training others, it was decided that Hanbury and the Flight Sergeant would stand-by as radar operators in two of the aircraft in case they had to be scrambled. They went off to rest whilst I, disappointed, went to the hangar to make sure the radar equipment was in the best possible state of performance.

In fact, the ground radar detection system covering the Thames Estuary did pick up raiders approaching at about 02.00 hrs and the two Blenheims were scrambled to attempt interceptions. As it happened, no interceptions were made but nevertheless a very important lesson was learned which was to have a major impact on the whole operation of night fighting using radar. It was fortunate that Hanbury had been involved in this first operational flight using radar and could realize, first hand, the almost impossible 'needle in a haystack' problem of intercepting using airborne radar with not more than a 3 or 4 mile range on the target aircraft.

As a result of his report it was quickly decided to develop a new ground radar especially designed to guide the night-fighters on to the raiding aircraft. This ground equipment became known as Ground Controlled Interception or GCI. Afterwards Hanbury described the flight in his usual style with typical humour. As I remember the story, his flight took off with almost no lighting aids on the airport and the whole country blacked out below them. They flew east at 18000 ft out over the coast, recognized by the white breaking surf. This height was dictated by the early radar needing to have a clear time base to the first sea reflection in which to see the target aircraft; this was a basic limitation of this early 1½ metre radar. After flying for some time and seeing nothing, the pilot turned on to the reciprocal bearing and headed back to the coast, but this did not appear at the estimated time of arrival (ETA). They continued to fly on but were getting increasingly anxious when all the guns in the Thames Estuary opened up at this lone aircraft which was making an unannounced entry into an extremely sensitive area. The aircraft had by chance flown directly up the middle of the Thames Estuary, where upon the pilot decided to climb to maximum height back out to sea and cruise around until it was light enough to land back at Northolt.

After this important event we spent the next two or three days at Northolt with the Blenheims on further training flights before leaving to join the rest of the Bawdsey team now trying to get themselves organized in the University of Dundee in Scotland.

Dundee and Perth

As I have already indicated, the whole Bawdsey Research Station, including my girlfriend and wife to be, Dorrie, vacated the Bawdsey site on 3 September 1939, the same day that Hanbury and I flew to Northolt with the Blenheims. This mass evacuation was all part of a well-planned move to Dundee University. The move had been planned to ensure this team and its radar equipments, vital to the war effort, were not destroyed by the German bombers in the early days of the war. The superintendent of BRS, then Mr A P Rowe – a somewhat cautious civil servant – made all these necessary arrangements after the Graf Zeppelin, during the previous July, had hovered 30 miles off the Bawdsey site for two or three days. Mr Rowe was sure that Hitler had a red circle around Bawdsey on his charts for one of the first bombing raids.

We, the airborne radar team, had to go north too, to Perth and nearby Scone airport where there was an airfield only just about big enough to operate aircraft like Fairy Battles, Lockheed Hudsons and Bristol Blenheims, etc. The airfield had a thriving flying training school of DH Moths, but was not really built to accommodate our more sophisticated aircraft, and many a close shave enlivened the crew room gossip. We stayed through September and October and managed to make some progress with our researches under very difficult circumstances. One development which Gerald Touch and I managed to complete at Scone was an automatic gain control circuit on our airborne receiver.

Hanbury, Bill Eastwood and I were billeted with the Laird of Scone in a large traditional Scottish manor house and were treated extremely well, having our own bedrooms and a common room for meals and sitting. The usual household staff of those days also waited on us. When it came to leave Scone we were genuinely sorry.

One other story of this period which is worth telling concerns the evacuation of BRS to Scotland on 3 September (three days later for Hanbury and me). Everyone set out with their own means of transport, cars or motorbikes. Many, like mine, were our first motorcars which, to say the least, were never intended to tackle the 400-odd miles to Dundee and Perth. Strangely, with a few difficult and some amusing incidents, all arrived. Even my square nosed 1927 Morris Oxford Coupé completed the journey handsomely. More about this car later after it had made a successful return to the South.

A colleague who ventured up to Dundee in a very old American Overland car found it in such bad shape on arrival that he decided to dump it. Rumour had it that, typically, he arranged to push it over a cliff in the hills north of Perth having charged several colleagues for attending the spectacle, which brought in more than he had paid for the car in the first place! Rumour or truth I never found out!

Having moved from Bawdsey to Dundee to be well away from the German bombers, the first bombs fell in Scotland near the Forth Bridge and our cautious Superintendent upped sticks and moved in October and November to Worth Matravers in Dorset at not a little disruption to the development of radar.

St Athan

Once again the airborne team moved, also in late October, not to Dorset but to a new airfield and maintenance unit being developed at St Athan in Wales just west of Cardiff. The situation on arrival was chaotic. Our unit was consigned to a very large new hangar which was only about 70% finished. The research and development work and the administrative work had to be carried out on benches erected in the single storey buildings along each side of the hangar with canvas screens along the sides of otherwise open areas in the hangar. These were both for security and protection from the elements. Water streamed through so that we had to have duck boards laid to avoid wet feet. This period was the start of the Royal Aircraft Establishment Farnborough [RAE] taking over from our research team the work of making installations of radar in Blenheims, Hudsons etc.

About this time I experienced the most impressive management excerise of my career. Lord Beaverbrook set up a team to speed up the production and development of equipment for the services. In his top management team Sir Robert Renwick was responsible for radio and radar and I attended his monthly meetings to cover ASV anti submarine and convoy control equipments. God help anyone who had not done what had been promised at the previous meeting!

One afternoon we suffered an alarming incident. A Blenheim standing in this closed but huge hangar undergoing maintenance suddenly spurted out several rounds from its four Browning machine guns. In the closed hangar the noise was deafening and we all thought it was a German raid. Fortunately, since the Blenheim had an old-fashioned three wheel undercarriage, the guns were pointing up and the bullets went up through the roof.

Some corporal airman sitting in the cockpit had idly pushed the trigger which had not been made safe after the last flight. There were a few on the verge of a nervous breakdown, including me!

In the short period during which we were at St Athan – we moved again early in 1941 to Farnborough – a number of events of interest are well worth putting on record. Firstly, several of our team were billeted in the Barry Island Dock Guest House. We were very welcome because otherwise in the middle of winter this holiday hotel had no other guests. During our stay I was able to share a garage at the back in which I carried out an engine strip down and decoke etc. of my faithful Morris in a mood of thank you after its faultless return from Scotland. This took up much of the evenings and weekends of the three or four months of our stay. When finished I put it into the local garage to have the brakes set up professionally. Imagine how devastated I was when, making the first run to the airfield at St Athan and descending a steep hill with a sharp bend at the bottom, application of the foot brake produced a terrible noise of metal being ill-treated. However, it was vital to slow for the sharp bend and another application of the foot brake caused the brake wires to part. The car roared down to the bend at the bottom, ran off the road, hit a fence of upright railway sleepers and turned over into a ditch. I was not hurt but as I scrambled out I remember a Welsh farm worker standing beside the upturned car saying "Indeed to goodness man can you not get out?" The car was a write-off and I bequeathed it to the garage who did such an 'excellent' job on the brakes. A sad parting.

During our stay in Wales I had quite a scary incident on a test flight in one of the Blenheims. The radar operator position in these night-fighters had, below it slightly to one side, an escape hatch which doubled as a camera support. Above it on the side of the fuselage the observer's parachute pack was stowed. On this occasion the hatch had not been secured and on taking off it was forced up at considerable velocity and cut the elastic containing straps of the parachute, whereupon the chute started to open in the rush of wind and threatened to fill the back of the aircraft. I spent a hectic few minutes struggling to contain this situation whilst the pilot flew round and landed. Not the least scary feature was a great hole in the bottom of the aircraft through which it would have been very easy to fall, had I put a foot wrong, so to speak.

Whilst at St Athan, several new research staff joined us from universities, Dr John Pringle from the Zoological Department at Cambridge, Dr Bernard Lovell from Manchester (later Sir Bernard Lovell of Jodrell Bank fame).

At this stage our small team was becoming stretched with installation work but one or two from RAE who were familiar with this type of work joined and one, Bob King, began to organize this work and he was joined by a gradual build up of RAE engineers. One interesting episode was the arrival of Bernard Lovell. I seem to remember he presented himself to us at a particularly busy time and, somewhat in desperation, Eddie Bowen, after greeting him, said "the stores here are a shambles and the greatest contribution you can make to the whole effort would be to organize them." Without any hesitation Bernard Lovell went off and did just that. In two or three weeks he had the stores situation greatly improved and came back for his next assignment. Eddie, appreciating how well this senior accademic had tackled this very menial but import-ant task, then gave him the exciting new research programme of developing airborne radar in the shorter centimetre wavelengths, which would offer much improved definition, smaller antennae, broader possibilities for applications and much improved perfor-mance all round.

Towards the end of this period at St Athan the team suffered their second fatal accident. One of the Hudson aircraft out on a test flight following the installation of ASV, crashed in the Welsh hills at the back of St Athan. All the crew were killed, including one of our more recent recruits named Beattie.

Pembroke Dock

During this stay at St Athan, John Pringle and I were given the task of designing homing and long range aerials on the new Sunderland flying boat for ASV Mk II operations in Coastal Command. We carried out this work on the slipway at the RAF flying boat station at Pembroke Dock which was convenient to the main airborne team at St Athan. We took about three weeks 'hanging' test aerials on various likely positions and taking polar diagrams around the aircraft on the slipway. We finished up with the usual three large Yagi arrays for homing operations and a broadside array of eight dipoles on streamlined metal posts on the top of the fuselage for transmitting sideways. A broadside array on each side of the fuselage for receiving used the aircraft hull as a reflector (Fig 18).

Whilst staying at the Pier Hotel in Pembroke Dock, John Pringle built quite a large (4ft wing span) model aircraft and started to fit it with an electronic control system. In those days such systems were very simple – crude compared with those of today – using 'bang/bang' relay arrangements. The hotel in those days was rather basic and had several resident mice whose presence was confirmed by bits on the tablecloth at breakfast time which were certainly not crumbs! For my part this assignment on the Sunderland brought me into close relationship with John Pringle and began a partnership which continued throughout the war years. As I have said already John was from the Zoological Dept of Cambridge University and had been researching into the mechanisms of control and behaviour in cockroaches. After the war I believe he was appointed to the Chair of Zoology at Oxford University. He was an education for me to be with and taught me to think in a logical fashion, which has helped me throughout my career.

18. Sunderland LRASV Aerials

RAE Farnborough

In the early spring of 1940 the airborne radar team was moved from St Athan and was, in fact, split. I, with Hanbury Brown, Gerald Touch, Roy Hearsum and one or two others were sent to the RAE at Farnborough to be part of their Radio Department to assist with engineering and overseeing of the production of 1½ metre ASV and A1. The others including Eddie Bowen, Bill Eastwood, Ron Taylor, Bernard Lovell, Alan Hodgskin etc. were incorporated into the Telecommunication Research Establishment (TRE) at Worth Matravers. Here they were to carry on the research and development [R and D] aimed to develop centimetre systems to exploit the higher accuracy and definition to be expected from these higher frequencies in the radio spectrum. This was the start of such equipments as Centimetre A1, H2S, etc.

RAE was a very different environment: easygoing compared to the one which we had inherited from BRS and which was

19. Boston Homing Aerials

maintained through Perth and St Athan. At RAE, in 1940, one would hardly realize the country was at war except that the Army was all around and they were well aware of it. For instance RAE Radio Department preserved the authorized Civil Service hours and avoided any urgent task outside the normal period. We had to organize quite a number of special arrangements in order to work early or late. My work tended to involve development of 1½ metre ASV and A1 aerials for various aircraft including the

65

Armstrong Whitworth Whitley, the Vickers Wellington, the Bristol Beaufighter and the Boston (Fig 19). This work was all done on the compass setting site on an area known as Jersey Brow.

One evening in late spring, two of us were working on Jersey Brow when we blew a main fuse on the site at the red distribution box. I walked over to replace the fuse and, at the exact moment I plugged it in, there was a tremendous explosion. At that moment I thought I had blown up half of RAE Farnborough. In fact it was the exact moment that the rocket team at RAE decided to test fire a loaded trolley on rails across the airfield.

Whilst at Farnborough Dorrie and I decided to marry and she left TRE and came to join me in Farnborough. We were married in the local church. I seem to remember it was during that period the Germans bombed the London Docks and from Farnborough it appeared that the whole of London was on fire – very spectacular but also very scary.

It is appropriate here to record some important thoughts about Dorrie. She has been a very loyal and devoted wife and mother in spite of several setbacks including a number of operations. She has a very strong character and is very determined when she has made up her mind on any point at issue. Of course the major problem which she and I, too, have had to face in both our lives has been concerning our daughter Judith. It was a difficult birth, causing damage which limited her physical development and resulted in her being unable to walk. Even so we both have to be very thankful that her mental faculties are of a high order. She gained A levels in Chemistry and Maths and a special in English. Judith held her place in a large girls public school and has been able to overcome the temptation to feel sorry for herself. Judith has inherited her mother's strength of character and is a calm and practical person. She has many friends. She has continuously carried out voluntary work on behalf of a number of organizations dedicated to raising awareness of the needs of disabled people and she chairs several committees at county level. Dorrie and I are very proud of our daughter and of what she has been able to achieve in spite of her many problems.

Of course the constant strain on Dorrie has been great and has added to the many demands on her. Nevertheless my wife is a perfectionist and throughout these sixty years has managed and maintained an almost spotless and very comfortable home leaving me free to pursue my many activities. Her love and understanding of animals and particularly dogs has always given her great pleasure and much of this love and understanding has been injected into both Judith and me.

Immediately after our marriage and in order to 'do her bit' for the war effort and also to help with the somewhat limited finances Dorrie took a position as personal assistant to the Chief of the Farnborough Fire Service.

During the period at RAE we took one or two of the Blenheims down to a night-fighter squadron at Tangmere on the south coast and undertook a number of tests and instruction flights. It was impressive to experience how those Blenheims behaved in the capable hands of those first-line fighter pilots.

One incident remains in my memory particularly. Having been thrown about in these aircraft practically all day I was walking one evening along the main street in Chichester with a colleague when we were accosted by a number of members of a highland regiment about to go overseas and we were given white feathers and berated as shirkers and 'conchies'. That took a great deal of 'turning the other cheek' but I suppose it was understandable. Eventually, they accepted that we were assisting the RAF, although we could not tell them how.

I had already indicated my desire to get back to TRE and, having briefed a number of influential people, including Gp Capt. King in the Air Ministry Operational Requirements Branch, I was at this stage posted back to Worth Matravers, much to my delight.

The Mission to Iceland

On return to TRE at Worth Matravers I prepared to settle down again in the research environment after the more engineering atmosphere of the RAE. I was given the task of developing a one piece overall test equipment for ASV II. I had spent a few weeks planning this and had just received a first prototype of the metal cabinet for installation of the various meters and components when I was sent for by the Superintendent, A P Rowe. He had received an urgent call from the Air Ministry that the Long Range ASV Whitney and Wellington aircraft in Iceland had suffered a serious decrease in their ASV performance during the few months since they were deployed and the RAF were calling for urgent help.

This situation was particularly serious since these aircraft with their sideways looking radar were able to cruise along the middle of the Denmark Strait – North of Iceland – and detect enemy ships attempting to enter the Atlantic from Northern Norway. The battle ships *Tirpets* and *Grieisenau* were, at the time, in Northern Norway poised to make such a dash into the Atlantic. I was asked to go to Iceland to sort out this problem and I was warned that any test flying would be on operations in a war zone with German U Boats very active. As a civilian I would be shot if picked up by the enemy so I was given an honorary short service commission as a Flying Officer. I was to leave as soon as possible and arrangements were made to depart from Hendon Airfield by RAF Ferry Command on the following afternoon. In the meantime I had to be kitted out at a tailors in Bournemouth as a Flying Officer, the arrangements for which had already been made. One other complication, I was having to leave my new wife of only two months who opted to go back to her parents in Felixstowe as I was expected to be in Iceland for at least two or three months. A staff car was arranged to take us to London next morning where I had to report to a Wing Commander Movements in Alexandria House in Kingsway.

My wife was to go on by train from Liverpool Street to her home in Felixstowe.

We arrived as planned at Alexandria House to report at 13.00 hours. I left my wife in the car and reported to a Warrant Officer who said his Wing Commander had gone to lunch, so I took my wife to lunch and saw her off at Liverpool Street. I then returned to Movements at 14.45 to be met by an irate Wing Commander who demanded to know why I was an hour late and even more so, why the blazes I had not saluted him on entering his office. He was so rude that this young civilian with no military training was provoked into saying 'the only salute I know is the Boy Scout's and you can have that, if you wish', The Wing Commander went puce, and when he got his breath back he hissed out to the Warrant Officer 'For God's sake get this man to Hendon and out of my sight'. A good start!

At Hendon I joined a small D H airliner being operated by Ferry Command for the flight to Prestwick. It was a comfortable plane and unusual in those days in that, I seem to recall, it had four small engines. If my memory is right it was an Albatross.

Prestwick was the largest international airport in the UK and had comfortable accommodation for overnight stopovers complete with bathrooms, lounge, bar etc. Having settled in I met the Ferry Command crew who were to take me and several others to Iceland in two days' time. The pilot, Flight Lt Brown, was an Englishman who before joining up had been flying for Air France. A very level headed and competent man whom I quickly learned to appreciate. The second pilot was a very amusing young man from the Polish air force. Competent, resourceful and great company. We were to experience a good example of his resourcefulness a little later. It had already been explained to us that at this time of the year (December) the air trip to Iceland was very closely scheduled. There were only very primitive landing lights at Reykjavik airport so the trip had to be completed within a very narrow window of daylight.

The distance from Prestwick of about 1000 miles was around the normal endurance of the Ferry Command Hudson aircraft being used. The Hudson was a new type from Lockheed and one of the first in the RAF to have a nose wheel, tricycle, type of undercarriage. British pilots, used to the types like the Anson with a tail wheel, had not got used to this very different landing configuration and there had already been a number of landing accidents on Hudsons as a result. Our crew were always referring to 'the bloody Hudson', which did not generate great confidence.

The flight to Iceland had to be carefully planned. Take off had to be before 09.00 hrs otherwise the flight had to be abandoned for the day. All concerned, crew and passengers, were called at 03.30 hrs and then went through a strict routine of breakfast, clearing en-route weather, emigration and customs. Then to board the aircraft, start-up, check engines, check radio communications, taxi out, and obtain take-off clearance to go. At any point in this sequence the whole flight had to be abandoned if each stage could not be completed within a very tight time slot. Of course the odds against a complete clearance in those days was quite high. So indeed it turned out to be. We all went through this schedule or part of it for twelve successive days with almost all permutations of problems until finally on 21 December, the shortest day and therefore the shortest daylight slot, we finally started to roll. This, after the Polish Second Pilot had marshalled all six passengers to sit together on top of heaps of mail bags etc around the main spar as near to the centre of gravity as possible. This, he explained, was because we were right up to top take-off weight this time. All the passengers and I must have been at the lowest ebb on our chances of a safe flight. In all my subsequent flying experience I have never been quite so sceptical about our chances of survival. I did at least have confidence in Brown and his colleague, having got to know them both well in our many jaunts around Ayr during our long wait at Prestwick. The ice rink at Ayr was the most popular of them all and my skating improved markedly.

As we began to roll along the runway we seemed to have leaden wings and just moments after we came unstuck I remember seeing the stone layered wall at the end of Prestwick main runway disappear under us with about ten feet to spare and a sigh of relief from me. However, our problems were by no means over. Slowly gaining height to negotiate the Outer Hebridean Islands, we reached 500 feet only to encounter severe icing. Large chunks were flying off the propellers and striking the fuselage. Further attempts to climb only increased this hazard and finally Brown decided to go out through the Islands below the icing and below 500ft – a very hazardous operation demanding extremely accurate navigation, but our Polish friend was equal to the task. After 500 miles and about halfway we broke out into brilliant sunshine and we were able to operate at the aircraft's normal cruising height and at its efficient fuel consumption. As a result we now have a much more relaxed aircrew and passengers. At this point our Polish friend went off to the back of the aircraft for the coffee flasks and sandwiches, but alas Prestwick caterers had forgotten to put them aboard. Now comes the good example of Polish resourcefulness. Unscrewing a panel in the floor he produced a box containing bottles of beer, loaves of black bread, a large black sausage and some cheese which he proceeded to carve up and pass around to all his passengers.

The remainder of the flight was uneventful. We landed nicely within our daylight slot and I caused some amusement by jumping out before the steps were deployed and, forgetting the apron was covered in ice, finally landed in Iceland sliding along on my bottom!

On arrival I was taken immediately to the officer commanding the RAF in Iceland, one Air Commodore Primrose. He and his Chief Signals Officer explained the situation with the ASV radar in the Whitley and Wellington aircraft and we immediately agreed a plan of attack on the problem starting with a flight in a Whitley

20. Whitley LRASV Aerials

(Fig 20) the next morning so that I could judge the situation for myself. Before sending me off to the adjutant to fix up quarters, the Air Commodore, in a very understanding manner, referred to my recent precipitation into uniform and suggested I might appreciate his adjutant giving me some instruction in military etiquette such as saluting etc., which he considered would make my life easier around the camp. What a different approach to the 'Boy Scout' situation that had been generated by W/Cdr Movements in London.

The test flight the following morning was uneventful, but the performance of the radar was very poor on both homing and long range aerials and we had to be within two or three miles of the Icelandic coast to acquire a readable blip from noise. The following examination on the ground placed the problem squarely with the aerials, and a test dipole aerial which the signals staff made up for me demonstrated that the transmitter/receiver equipment was operating normally. The next move was to inspect one of the feeders by removing it from the aircraft for examination. In these early days of radar the feeders were made up of a copper wire inner sitting within a copper tube and supported every six inches by porcelain beads. When we removed the inner wire and its beads, in this case, a large amount of copper sulphate crystals fell out which had been acting as a short circuit to the radio frequency energy. There was no sealing arrangement and in the very wide range and frequency of change of temperature and of humidity, the breathing in and out of the atmosphere had produced this build-up of crystals. Fortunately, before leaving TRE a great friend and colleague, the previously mentioned Gerard Touch, had suspected trouble of this kind. He was, at the time, developing some of the first polythene filled cable and insisted I bring a large roll of his first delivery with me to Iceland. With the willing assistance of the signals staff, we set about recabling the homing and long range aerials on the Whitley normally used by the Air Commodore. Conditions in Iceland at this time of the year were very unpredictable and varying from mild drenching rain to snow and icing at a frequency which was quite incredible, and rewiring feeders in minus 10 degrees on an aircraft out on the airfield required a stoicism well above anything I had experienced previously – even keeping soldering irons hot with blowlamps became an art in itself.

However, after four days hard work in very trying conditions we were ready for an air test. The Air Commodore himself decided to take us up. Judge the elation of all on board when, even as we left the coast, we were able to track a very strong pulse echo return from the coast and 'see' a number of ships in a resting convoy a few miles out.

Finally, on both homing and long range aerials, we were receiving the echo from the Icelandic coast up to some forty-five miles away. This was much better by nearly ten miles than the performance when the aircraft were first delivered. Of course, much of this improvement was directly due to the new polythene cable which had a much lower attenuation factor than the previous copper tube feeders. Also the new cable could not breathe and therefore the improved performance could be expected to be maintained.

However, naturally, to the local RAF at all levels, that chap Flying Officer Wood was a genius, and there was a great celebration in the Officers' Mess that evening and four of us went into Reykjavik to the dance at the Borg Hotel. This was interesting since all the girls had to sit at separate tables from the men and were only permitted to dance with the opposite sex but not to sit with them. There certainly were an unusual number of rather outstanding blondes but also some very fine dark girls with Eskimo lineage. Incidentally there was a difficult situation concerning the large number of American forces in Iceland at that time and the local young men. The latter had a difficult time trying to overcome the effects of the inevitable attractions which unlimited nylons and cigarettes had on many of their womenfolk. This led to some unfortunate incidents.

Christmas was quite an experience and festivities in the Officers' Mess seemed to be continuous from Christmas Eve through to the day after Boxing day. One long period of eating, drinking, and occasionally sleeping. Playing rugby with a red cabbage as a ball and taking part in the 'Wall of Death' were just two of the diversions. This latter involved running around three sides of the mess lounge and planting one's foot as high up the remaining wall as possible. This game was banned later after one or two broken collarbones!

It was during Christmas with the RAF in Iceland that I was really drunk for the first and last time in my life. [I hope!] I had spent Boxing Day evening still enjoying all the festivities, which started at lunch on Christmas day. At two in the early hours, I had had more than enough and decided to retire to my Nissen hut quarters which normally were occupied by a Wing Cdr, who was away on leave in the UK. As I walked from the Officers' mess, which was very warm, into the clear cold night at about minus 12 degrees, the change of temperature hit me between the eyes. I staggered the two or three hundred yards to the hut and straight on to the bed only to have the sensation that it was rotating faster and faster, and I felt very ill. I reeled out of the door again and was violently ill all over the step and entrance. I then retired to bed, again oblivious to anything. The Batman wakened me at 07.00 with the inevitable cup of strong tea. If he reacted to my dreadful state of disarray he showed no signs. All I could think about was the dreadful mess outside the Wing Cdr's quarters. Judge my delight when, on emerging into the cold morning, there had been a considerable snowfall overnight and all the evidence had been obliterated!!

After Christmas the installation work on the Whitleys proceeded well, with the RAF Signals staff becoming increasingly competent. Each completed installation was flight tested before handing over to the squadron. However, in one case we were some fifty miles off the Icelandic coast when we 'lost' an engine whilst flying at about 1000ft. This type of aircraft had a poor performance on one engine and in order to make the airport at Reykjavik the crew went around with an axe and removed every piece of equipment that was not essential for flight. This was standard drill in these circumstances. We made the runway but you can imagine my feelings as all my carefully aligned ASV equipment was dumped overboard into the North Atlantic.

By February I began to sense the possibility of returning to the UK. This I looked forward too, since Iceland was hardly an attractive place in winter and my new wife was getting restive. In Iceland there were no trees, sheep feeding on the seaweed giving the meat a kind of iodine flavour, and the climate was exasperating and almost unpredictable from day to day. A visit to the hot geysers behind Reykjavik was interesting and, in view of the usual winter temperature, quite incongruous. There were stories of greenhouses growing tomatoes and exotic fruits, but I didn't see any. The super heated water from the geyser area was piped through the town through special low loss pipes. Householders were connected to this utility rather in the same way as the gas and electricity. The specially designed low loss pipes, manufactured in Denmark, were quite remarkable and a section of pipe was on show in the town.

There was still another unexpected job to do. The Air Commodore asked me to accompany him on a flight to demonstrate the ASV to his opposite number in charge of the American Air Force in Iceland – one Commander Carney of the U S Navy – who had his headquarters in a flying boat 'mother' ship called the *Belnap* from which he controlled squadrons of PBY [Catalina] and PBM [Mariner] flying boats. The Americans, although well up with ground radar at this time, had hardly considered airborne radar and the Commander was very interested and much impressed. This episode was to generate a very important development for me later when I returned to the UK.

I left Iceland in late February with all the Whitley squadron serviceable and with the improved performance. Just before leaving we experienced a freezing hurricane with winds over eighty knots in gusts. All the RAF personnel, including me, turned out in parties on a rota over a period of nearly twenty-four hours. This was to help hold down the aircraft out on the open airfield which were lifting on their undercarriages and almost flying. Ropes were slung over the wings with teams of men on each end to prevent them 'flying'. During the rest periods in the Officers' Mess there was much amusement watching all ranks crawling about on their hands and knees when the gusts were at the maximum. At one point the RAF at Reykjavik received a signal from RAF Kaldarnes on the other side of the mountains which read 'WT Nissan Hut airborne 11.00 hrs ETA Reykjavik 11.15 hrs.'

Two days after this I embarked for home on the Polish cruise liner SS *Batory* which was operating as a troop ship. It was an exciting voyage since the ship was just solo with one escort destroyer and capable of a speed which did not require her to be in convoy. We had several calls to emergency lifeboat stations during the voyage because of submarine alerts. On one occasion our destroyer escort dropped back and laid depth charges but there were no obvious results and we arrived safely in the Clyde off Greenock.

I had shared a cabin with one Fl/Lt Ericsson on the voyage. Ericsson was a chain smoker and took every opportunity to buy cigarettes and nylon stockings. This led to an amusing incident with customs, which I expected to clear on shore as was normal in my previous experience. When ordered ashore Ericsson went ahead of me through the foyer of the ship in one corner of which were tables stacked with cigarettes and nylons and he made straight for these. Thinking this was just true to form and a last opportunity to purchase I shouted to him as I passed him to descend the gangway down to the lighter. "I don't want any more cigarettes and nylons, I've got a suitcase full already". A few minutes later Ericsson appeared. "My God", he said, "you're a cool customer that was customs upstairs and they just charged me fifteen quid!"

Helensburgh and the Catalina

Having developed both homing and long range aerial arrays for a large number of different aircraft at RAE I was quite unexpectedly asked to develop a full system for an American PBY Catalina flying boat. Later I learned that this request was triggered by the demonstration Air Cdr Primrose and I had given to the American Commander in Iceland. This project was being organized by a Group Captain King of the Air Ministry Operation Requirements Branch. The aircraft had been delivered to the Marine Aircraft Experimental Establishment which was no longer at Felixstowe but relocated on the Gareloch in Scotland. Its headquarters and administration had taken over the premises of the Royal Northern Yacht Club at Rhu near Helensburgh. Roy Hearsum and I travelled to Scotland by overnight sleeper and were accommodated in the MAEE Sergeants' Mess. The aircraft was positioned on a large slipway with a very large concrete circular pad at the shore end. I had to persuade the Commanding Officer, Group Captain Oddie, to let us occupy this choice site against a number of other operational needs. We needed it in order to take the polar diagram measuring equipment around the aircraft. Other sites would have required Wellington boots wading in quite deep mud on the river bank. Even so, the work was difficult. This aircraft sat very low in the water and was a high winged monoplane to enable the two engines to be installed sufficiently above the water to avoid swamping them on the take-off and landing. Thus we obviously had a major problem as to where to put the aerials. We were able to get the MAEE to take some pictures of the take-off and landing on a fairly rough sea state and it was immediately clear that we had a new problem to solve. It would be necessary to make all the long range broadside aerials sufficiently strong to survive the worst conditions. The homing aerials could be normal Yagi types since they could be slung under the high wing and well clear of the water (Figs 21 and 22).

When the design was complete we liaised closely with the Saunders Rowe plant at Beaumaris in Anglesey and a full installation was made and tested successfully around the islands off the West coast of Scotland. Group Captain King wrote a letter to TRE praising my work and recommending I returned to TRE rather than RAE, and surely enough I received a letter to return to Worth Matravers where I could rejoin my wife, whom I had seen only infrequently since we were married. The work we did in Helensburgh was to stand us in good stead on our next assignment. The project had taken about one month and had

21. Catalina Starboard Homing Aerial

22. Catalina LRASV Aerials

involved several journeys on the overnight sleeper to Glasgow. On one of these I experienced a German bombing raid whilst the train was standing in Crewe station, and it was very frightening in the middle of the night.

Two interesting asides are worth recording during this period. Firstly, Group Captain Oddie, in charge of MAEE, was a disciplinarian and every Saturday morning the whole camp had to undertake a four mile route march around Helensburgh. Roy Hearsum and I only avoided this by appealing to Group Captain King on the basis of urgent war work. I was very popular because the Air Ministry letter releasing us from the march included the whole team involved in the Catalina programme.

The other story involved my unwise acceptance of an invitation by one of the flight sergeants. He invited me one Sunday to join him and one of his colleagues on a cross country walk from Helensburgh to Loch Lomond. What I did not know was they were both Suffolk Harriers whilst stationed previously in Felixstowe. I don't think I have ever been so tired at the end of a day in my life. Of course the scenery was out of this world, so to speak. One thing which also impressed itself on me was that coming back, mainly down steep contours, was more difficult than toiling up on the way there. The compulsion to let oneself go faster and faster was quite frightening at times on some of the steeper inclines. However, I lived to tell the tale and it was quite an outstanding experience.

TRE Worth Matravers

The Catalina project successfully completed, Group Captain King had kept his word and the Superintendent of TRE Worth Matravers, Mr AP Rowe, welcomed me back to his team on airborne radar at Leeson House. I was very pleased to be back among many friends and colleagues. Much had changed, however, and I was given the task of developing a test equipment for checking out ASV II equipment. Not very exciting but it enabled me to rejoin my wife again. We were fortunate to be able to hire a very attractive house on the edge of the downs at Swanage. My wife had come down from Dundee with the others and had been staying with friends in a bungalow further up the downs. However, this rather pleasant situation did not last very long. Within a few weeks Mr Rowe received a request through the Air Ministry from the US Navy for me to take a fitted Catalina with LRASV to America for demonstrations to both the American Air Force and the Navy. It was also planned to organize the installation of the ASV II equipment for the American forces by firms like Consolidated Aircraft, Boeing and Lockheed and for the fitting of the lend-lease aircraft being supplied to the RAF in the UK. Commander Carney was obviously behind this request and I was to receive VIP treatment.

A Catalina had been fitted to our plans at Saunders Rowe in their new wartime factory at Beaumaris in Anglesea. Meanwhile, I was given First Class Pan American Clipper tickets from Lisbon to New York on the regular commercial service via Brazil, Trinidad, Puerto Rico and Bermuda, to go out immediately to plan for the reception of the Catalina aircraft and to organize the programme of ASV installations in USAF aircraft, such as their Boeing Flying Fortress, the Lockheed Liberator, the Consolidated PBY Catalina etc. I would also be expected to assist the Mission, and Gerald Touch in particular, to make all the arrangements necessary for the American radio industry to produce ASV airborne equipment in quantity to boost the supplies for both the USAF, the US Navy and the RAF.

Chapter 5

Early Airborne Radar at War [1943–1945]

Mission to America

In order that younger readers can appreciate fully the very special nature of this journey I was about to undertake, and particularly the flight in the Pan American flying boat, they may need a reminder of the state of air travel at that time. Long ocean crossings were practical and sufficiently safe only by flying boat. Even so flying to America, westbound, because of strong prevailing Westerly head winds, the shortest ocean crossing had to be used from West Africa to South America. During the war land planes such as the four engined Liberators on delivery flights demonstrated the reliability of such aircraft which, of course, were much easier to operate with increasing flexibility. This, sadly, meant the demise of the beautiful flying boats. I considered myself to have been most fortunate, indeed privileged, to have experienced and enjoyed this peak period in the operation of the flying boat in civil aviation.

On Monday 10 April 1942 I set out for the USA. This journey was a story in itself. I travelled to Barnstaple via Bristol to join the free Dutch KLM service which they had started to operate regularly from Barnstaple airport to Lisbon. We had an uneventful trip in the DC3 to Cintra airport near Lisbon. I say we, because travelling with me was a young American named Rock who was in the UK to gain experience of airborne radar of which, as I have said before,

America knew very little at that time.

We were met in Lisbon and delivered to our respective Embassies which had responsibility for us during our stay in Lisbon. This was expected to last two or three days only. In fact, we were there for about two weeks, the reason for which I will explain shortly. A very important subject of the briefing was to warn me not to talk to anyone about the bombing damage in the UK and, particularly at that time, the effect of parachute land mines. We had been booked into the Palacio Hotel in Estoril, a very high class establishment which in wartime was a hive of intrigue. Portugal was neutral and Lisbon, in particular, was full of spies of many nations. Rock and I had both been warned that a number were living in our hotel and, in particular, a party of so-called Lufthansa airline crews was made up a of a variety of German airforce officers and members of Goebbel's secret police etc. and could be expected to have a table beside ours in the main restaurant.

This atmosphere literally went to young Rock's head. He cadged some US Embassy headed notepaper and envelopes and hid them in his room under the mattress, under the carpet and in a suitcase which he had 'wired up' with cotton. The latter was often found broken but I suspected it got broken in the act of closing the case 'very carefully'! Again, hoping to catch a spy, almost invariably as we entered the palatial lobby of the hotel, six foot Rock would burst into a run and leap up the grand staircase two at a time. He would appear minutes later saying something like "Gee – damn it – I just missed him and I heard the door bang as I was going up the stairs." As I said, we were due to leave on the scheduled clipper flight two days after arrival in Lisbon. However, on the day before we were to leave, the American Embassy in Vichy France broke off normal diplomatic relationships and withdrew the staff. As a result, all the clipper flights for about two weeks were taken up by holders of priority diplomatic passports and Rock and I were instructed to wait until they were cleared. I sent a signal from the

Embassy to Watson-Watt in the Air Ministry explaining the situation and asking him to facilitate and 'get me out of here'. A reply was received saying stay put and catch the first available flight. Rock had a somewhat similar instruction from his headquarters.

Consciences satisfied, we both settled down to a routine of tennis, swimming and exploring Lisbon. I remember so well the very striking Avenidada Liberdade running up the middle of the city from the Tagus river with its huge dual carriageway separated by a central reservation nearly as wide and covered in camelias and palms of all kinds. We also fell in love with Cascais, a little unspoilt fishing village at the mouth of the Tagus. I wonder if it is still unspoilt or has it been changed beyond recognition by tourism? We also visited the castle of Cintra by horse carriage with its spectacular view at the top on all sides and the building full of beautiful antiques and interesting artefacts.

We went to the bullfight in the large stadium in the north end of the city. As very much an animal lover this was against my better judgement. However, I was in for a very pleasant surprise as I will explain. The performance began with much pomp and ceremony and great blowing of horns as about eight brightly dressed men looking like a rugby scrum entered the ring. They were followed by a young very active bull who immediately took exception to the men and charged at each one in turn. None stood their ground but leaped over the safety fence. I seem to recall seeing their multicoloured bottoms disappearing one after the other only to return again over the fence to face another charge. When this very virile young animal had slowed down a little, one man (the hooker?) decided to stand his ground and as the bull charged he allowed himself to go backwards with the charge whilst hooking his arms around the bull's horns and his legs around its jaws. At this point all the others held on to legs and tail and brought the bull's charge to a halt in the middle of the ring. The men then peeled off leaving two on the tail. Finally the bull pulling one way and the men pulling the other let go and disappeared over the safety fence. At this point the bull was furious, when in came an immaculate horse and rider combination and using the ultimate in riding skill the bull was teased and had darts stuck into his hide in mock swordsmanship. The dart indicated where the 'kill' strike would have been delivered. The show of horsemanship was incredibly graceful and in charge after charge the bull did not get anywhere near striking the horse. Finally the horse and rider made a measured retreat out of the ring leaving an enraged and perplexed young bull! One started to wonder how such an enraged animal can be got out of the ring, when in came a herd of cows with bells around their necks and the bull got linked up with them and went out of the ring like a lamb.

Hence my very pleasant surprise and great pleasure to find that the bull was not killed and only its pride was hurt. The horsemanship was exceptional. I understand the horseman's career is ruined if there should be the smallest scratch on the horse. I enjoyed the Portuguese bullfight.

One very amusing incident which happened before we finally were booked on to a clipper flight occurred the night before at dinner in the palatial restaurant of the Palacio. I was sitting with others of the UK party just about to start the meal and Rock was late (deliberately as it turned out!) After we had all started and practically the whole restaurant was full, including the 'Lufthansa' people at the next table, six foot Rock bounded into the dining room waving a copy of the *Daily Telegraph*. He rushed up to me shouting "Woodie, this will do your heart good"! On the back of the paper that day half the page was taken up by a picture of the devastation of Rostock from the first one thousand RAF bomber raid. You could have cut the atmosphere between the two tables with a knife!

The next day we joined the *Atlantic Clipper* on the Tagus and took off in the early evening on the first stage of our journey to New York. The accommodation was sumptuous with two decks and a part of the top deck serving as a bar and a dining room. I do not remember exactly but I think there were about 15–20 passengers. Rock and I quickly became friendly with an American lawyer named Taylor and his wife and with a Dr Chang who was an advisor on finance in the Chinese Embassy in Washington. Later in the evening we had dinner, which was memorable for a line of conversation with Dr Chang on the writing of Chinese, which he explained was originally the prerogative of the upper classes. It was full of personal artistic flourishes. Inevitably he was asked to illustrate how he would deal with modern words like 'television' for instance. I asked how he would write 'battleship'. He drew his illustration on a PanAm paper serviette which I still have. He drew two matchstick men with squares for heads. The mouths were straight lines and the eyes dots. He then opened one mouth by drawing a small rectangle – a discussion! Then producing a rectangle for the other man's mouth – an argument! The argument was turned into a fight by drawing a symbol for a paddy field above them – the Chinaman's all. The symbol was completed with a long boat with oars stood up on end beside the two men.

We flew the 1650 miles at about 150mph overnight and at dawn found ourselves descending along the West Coast of Africa to land at Bolama in Senegal where we went ashore to the local rest house for breakfast. We spent the day in this rather primitive town and Taylor, Rock and I did a tour of the locality after lunch. The native population were very dark in colour, almost jet black. Many had limbs which were distorted from breaks which had not been properly reset. I remember helping myself to a mango from a tree we were passing and, after a cursory wipe with my handkerchief, eating it on the spot. Although, in this germ-conscious age, this would be regarded as foolhardy, I have never tasted such a delicious fruit.

Once again the *Clipper* took off from Bolama in the early evening on its 1450 mile journey across the South Atlantic to Natal in Brazil. The dinner was again full of interesting exchanges with Dr Chang suggesting that young men like Rock and I should consider China when the war was over as his country would be expanding rapidly and in need of trained professionals in electronics and communications. Looking back he was, in many ways, correct. We landed in Natal for breakfast at an hotel and later continued our journey around midday to Belem (now Para) at the mouth of the Amazon River. Here we were placed in the Grand Hotel and remained in Belem for two days awaiting clearance of cyclones in the Caribbean. During our stay a May Day carnival with many elaborately bedecked floats took place which we watched sipping cocktails from the pavement café outside the hotel. The floats were very colourful and full of beautiful girls. This was too much for Rock and suddenly he leaped up, ran across the street and jumped onto the nearest float. That was the last the Taylors and I saw of him until the next morning. We stayed two days in all with mosquito nets at night, which were essential. Imagine my horror when, on the first morning, I went over to the wash basin only to find a large snake twisted around the cold water pipe leading down to the basin. It reared its head and hissed at me. The snake was hardly surprising since in those days one wall of my room had about a one foot gap between it and the ceiling for ventilation. A call to reception produced a servant with a small forked stick and the incident was efficiently dealt with.

On 3 May we were on our way again over the Amazon Delta to Trinidad in the West Indies. Flying at about 5000ft for a very long time over this enormous geological feature, namely the Amazon Delta, was very impressive. The mixture of green jungle and forest stretched inland and extended as far as the eye could see. Here and there we had short glimpses of one of the larger tributaries, almost lost in jungle. Later in my career I had similar flights across the deltas of the Mississippi and the Ganges; all very different. The Mississippi with all the signs of modern industry around its coastline; the Ganges flat and brown with mud and silt from inland India.

Landing at Port of Spain in Trinidad in the early evening we were taken to the Park Hotel for the night, but again problems with the weather extended our stay by two days. Compared with the other stops after Lisbon this was delightful with a lovely atmosphere and lots of sun and breeze. My room in the Park Hotel overlooked the home of West Indies test matches and lots of park cricket pitches which seemed to be in constant use. Port of Spain was pleasant and green with a slightly old world atmosphere. After a lazy pleasant stay in Trinidad we departed for Puerto Rico. As we landed the sea was full of small yellow 'balls' which turned out to be thousands of grapefruit from a freighter torpedoed recently by a German U Boat just off the coast. The clipper threw them out in all directions as it landed! We made a comparatively short stop in San Juan mainly for refuelling and set out on an overnight flight to Bermuda. As usual there was the now routine dinner with its variety of subjects and varied exchanges. Coming in to land in Bermuda in the early morning of a very nice day the island looked very attractive, and it would have been nice to have had at least a few hours there, but this was not to be and after refuelling we set off again for New York. We landed on the Hudson river beside the famous Wall Street Skyline at lunchtime.

From leaving Barnstaple airport to landing in New York had been a journey of about 21 days. I was not conscious of this unique situation at the time but looking back I had been one of a comparatively small number of early passengers to be part of pioneering long distance cross-ocean air travel. We had travelled in luxury in this quite magnificent Boeing *Atlantic Clipper* flying boat, which behaved impeccably throughout the journey. It is worth pointing out one of the unusual features of this aircraft. In place of the usual wing tip floats to effect lateral stability whilst on the water this aircraft had dorsal stabilizers extending out from the centre fuselage. This seemed to me much more effective in that lateral movement was damped out earlier and the stabilizers also provided useful platforms for entering and leaving the aircraft.

I, personally, was sad to see the comparatively early demise of the flying boat airliners which had to give way to the large land planes which, with the reliability of four engines, proved to be much more flexible in practice and easier to operate. Now of course, it is quite normal to cross oceans with land planes with only two engines. So much has the reliability of the aero engine improved during the last forty or fifty years.

On arrival in New York I was met by a member of the British Mission and taken to the Commodore Hotel for an overnight stay to rest and 'recover' from the long journey. It was planned for me to fly to Washington from La Guardia airport next day. However, I could not resist seeing something of this great city and did a tour of Harlem, Central Park and Broadway during the afternoon and evening. I also went to the top of the Empire State Building. Walking down Broadway I was very amused when glancing in a shop window, there was a notice 'we fix flats'. The shop was selling ladies lingerie!!

I flew to Washington the next morning, (5 May) and reported to Mr Barton, Head of the British Air Commission (BAC) in a large building in Massachusetts Avenue. I also renewed my relationship with my old colleague and friend of Bawdsey days, Gerald Touch, who I was expecting would assist with 1½ metre airborne radar work as part of his work in the Mission. There were several other ex Bawdsey colleagues in the Mission team including Richard Davies on IFF (Identification Friend or Foe), Ken Budden on Ground Radar and, a little later, Roy Hearsum, joining me on airborne radar. A number of us had rooms in a nearby hotel called the Graylin run by a very affable Englishman who was keen to make his fellow nationals comfortable.

During my stay of some 5 months in the USA I was to cross the continent at least ten times by air and on all three main routes. United Airlines operated the Northern route via Ohio, Chicago and Salt Lake City to Portland in Washington State. TransWorld Airlines plied the centre ground to Kentucky, Nashville, Kansas and San Francisco. American Airlines operated the southern route via New Orleans, Dallas, New Mexico to Los Angeles. Airline travel was already well developed in America and they used, almost exclusively, the trusty 'work horse', the DC3 produced by the Douglas Aircraft Corporation. Passengers were still being treated exceptionally well as all the carriers were still building their reputations. I was always struck by the wallets invariably placed in a pocket on the back of the seat in front. These contained a picture of the airliner, a map of the routes operated, a timetable giving all the airlines services and not the least item – the sick bag! Since, in these early days, the aircraft rarely flew above 10,000 feet and were often in turbulence and cloud, this was an essential item. I can claim to have used it on only one occasion, when I chose a TransWorld Airlines flight to California with a special diversion to see the Grand Canyon. Very inadvisedly, just before reaching this famous landmark, we were served with strawberry sundaes, and practically all the passengers were ill. Fortunately my problem did not begin until we had almost completed the crossing so at least I did not miss the spectacle. Flying at just below the lip of the canyon was very turbulent indeed, but very spectacular.

On arrival in Washington, Barton, Touch and I discussed plans for my work programme which was expected to take several months. The main tasks were to advise and assist the aircraft manufacturers to select aerials and aerial sites for 1½ mtr ASV, to help plan the equipment installations and to carry out ground and flight tests of the prototypes. The aircraft involved were the

Catalina at the Consolidated Aircraft Corporation at San Diego, the Hudson at the Lockheed Corporation at Burbank, the B17 and the B37 at the Boeing Aircraft Corporation in Seattle. Interlaced in between these projects I was expected to visit several US Navy and USAF establishments to give presentations on the ASVII equipment and operation and also to attend a number of conferences.

Meanwhile, Gerald Touch, who was on a secondment from RAE for a period, had been assisting and was continuing to advise and assist several major radio manufacturers such as Bendix, to produce the ASV II transmitter/receiver equipment. Although my general programme was clear one could only plan each week ahead and the efficient way in which the BAC officers and secretaries in Washington, Dayton, Beverly Hills and in Canada arranged my travel itinerary and accommodation was a very large factor in my being able to achieve my very full programme successfully in the time. I don't remember one major hitch.

In a period of about five months I made 19 major journeys, mainly by civil airlines, but two or three by train. In the same period I took part in several quite long test flights over the Atlantic, the Caribbean, the Pacific and the Great Lakes, checking out prototype ASVII installations.

Before I get very involved describing my work in America in more detail I think I should explain the general environment, just in case the reader gets the impression that it was all receptions, parties and beach expeditions. At this time, America was a country still in the full enjoyment of peace. This, coupled with the fact that I found the Americans almost invariably friendly and very hospitable, led to innumerable invitations to parties of all kinds and many enjoyable experiences at dinner in American homes. Thus, throughout my stay, although a great deal of effort was devoted to my exacting work programme, I was constantly involved in social activities and this, to a considerable extent, was provoked further by my RAF Honorary Commission uniform. Very few RAF officers had been seen outside New York and Washington at that time in early 1941.

All this made my itinerary doubly demanding!

From 6 to 10 May I spent in Washington at BAC, the US Navy Department, and at the Air Force Bureau giving presentations and making plans for those parts of the visit which involved flying including security clearance.

On 11 May I departed by air to San Diego via St Louis, Boulder City and Los Angeles. This journey was the eye opener, so to speak. We were travelling through the night making several stops, and with the frequent take-offs and landings it was very short, disturbed sleep. We started rather amusingly on take-off from La Guardia airport. Hearsum was travelling with me and, just for fun, we agreed to use our local accents; my Suffolk dialect and his from Essex. Although America was not yet in the war, just as a precaution all blinds had to be drawn before take-off and before landing to make it difficult to get familiar with the layout of the airports. Imagine the look on the face of the beautiful TWA hostess when my first words were: 'Doon't you draw them they ode blinds gal, I can't see nauthin!!' The air hostesses were all beautiful in those early days – the very pick of the bunch. We kept this up until the crew changed at St Louis and I've never had so many offers of drinks at the several intermediate stops. It was on this first flight that we flew over the Grand Canyon with the unpleasant result I related earlier.

On 13 May, having changed planes at Los Angeles we arrived at San Diego at lunchtime and checked in at the El Cortez hotel. After lunch we reported at the Consolidated Aircraft Corporation who were producing the PBY Catalina and the PBM Mariner flying boats. This first exercise was expected to be more straightforward than my later assignments since our work on the Catalina at Helensburgh meant that we had all the Saunders Roe drawings and designs. The Resident Technical Officer (RTO), Mr Cooper, and a team from the firm's engineering staff, planned the work and the timetable in detail over the next three days. During this period I was also scheduled to visit the US Naval establishment at their base on North Island in the Bay. They sent a launch for me and I gave an ASV presentation to a large gathering. This visit resulted in my being invited to a dinner in the Officers' Club. After dinner a group of young officers decided to take me over the border into Mexico at a place called Tijuana and to a night club which claimed fame as owners of a highly polished chrome dance floor. All dancers were issued with the airline type slippers in order to avoid scratches, etc. The claim was that many of the girls wore no knickers, which could be quite a spectacle! However, the dance floor, in my limited experience, was so crowded and it was normal in those days for partners to dance close together, thus I was not able to confirm the claim one way or another. Having completed our planning and presentations at Consolidated we left San Diego for Burbank and the Lockheed Vega Company who were making the Hudson aircraft.

One interesting observation about San Diego. In the four days, there was never a cloud in the sky and the temperature was in the high eighties So much so that I began to long for a foggy day in London!

Having visited both the aircraft company and North Island again early on 15 May, I then left by air for Los Angeles and the Bilmore Hotel. Next morning I visited the Lockheed Vega plant at Burbank and met the RTO, a Mr Wheeler. Here again I could call on work we had done in the UK to install the ASV II facility in the Hudson aircraft. We discussed with the design office staff and agreed the main features for detailed planning purposes. The next morning I visited the BAC office in Beverly Hills and met Bill Yearsly who was in charge. He had fixed me up with a room in the Roosevelt Hotel in Hollywood and we dined together and I had a quick tour of the sights. The next morning I had a meeting again at the Lockheed plant where we finalized the programme for the lend-lease Hudsons for delivery to the RAF. Later that afternoon I departed by air again for San Francisco and the Sir Francis Drake hotel. This assignment in Frisco was to lecture on 1½ metre airborne radar at the US Navy station at Alameda nearby. Typically I was telephoned very soon after arrival by the Head of Signals from the naval air station who decided to join me for dinner. He arrived with three other officers and we dined in the hotel restaurant. After an interesting meal and even more interesting conversation, mainly about life in the US Navy, they decided, as had their colleagues at North Island, San Diego, to take me to one of their favourite night spots called The Forbidden City. This was well 'upmarket', so to speak, to the one at Tijuana and had a floor show of Chinese girls. They were carefully picked and were tall and elegant and completely changed my vision of Chinese women gathered from the normal western portrait of them in drab blue uniforms.

The next day I gave my presentation at Alameda to quite a large audience of naval officers with radio and signals duties together with some pilots. During the day I received a call from Lockheed to call in at Burbank again on the way back to Washington. Later, on 21 May, having called in and cleared the problem at Lockheed, I departed for Washington on a night flight via La Guardia.

I was in Washington for four days reporting and visiting the Navy and Airforce departments for a further series of discussions and planning.

In the evening I was entertained by Gerald Touch and his wife and in the next day or two we made visits to the Washington Zoo and to the Barnum and Bailey's Three Ring Circus. The latter was a typical America 'big'. Frankly, in some ways, I was disappointed since there was no way one could see more than a third of what was going on at any one moment. Of course, what one was able to concentrate on was fabulous, which made missing so much even more irritating.

I also met, for the first time, a communications expert from the radio department of the RAE Farnborough – one Bill Mackinson. I did not know at the time that he would be a future boss. After the war, at one stage, he became head of the BLEU (Blind Landing Experimental Unit) at Martlesham Heath for a period. Bill was a heavily built chap and an ex RAF boxer. We became very good friends and spent several pleasant evenings in his 'pet' Washington restaurant 'The Balalaika'. This, as one might expect, was Russian and had several excellent cabaret acts including a knife thrower and a troupe of dancers specializing in the bent knee exercises for which that country is famous.

Before getting into the work programme again I have to record how impressed I was with the American capital. The centre laid out like a cross with the Lincoln Memorial at one end, the Capitol Building at the other, the Jefferson Memorial at the end of one arm and the Monument in the centre with the White House on the other arm. The Jefferson attracted me particularly – perhaps because I like curves! It was May and all the cherry trees were in blossom around the lake in front of the memorial – a truly memorable sight. I was told that there is always one week in May dedicated to those trees coming into blossom and artificial processes are brought into play to either speed up the blossom burst or to delay it so that it occurs during the right week in the calendar and visits can be planned.

On 25 May I was off again with Roy Hearsum and Bill Yearsly by overnight train to Dayton, Ohio and Wright Patterson experimental air base. We arrived early next day and were met by staff from the local BAC office. We were booked in the Van Cleve Hotel and had lunch in the 'Flagship' restaurant which was quite unusual in that within the large dining room was erected the full scale – I think it was full scale – fuselage of a DC3 airliner.

Some tables were under the truncated wings, some had propeller blades coming down into the table centre. Other tables were lit by the landing lights. It was quite unusual, to say the least, and very effective. Later in the visit it was in the Flagship that one of our English visitors, finding a very full hat stand, threw off an American army officer's cap to make room for his coat, and we only just avoided an unpleasant incident.

At Wright Patterson we were involved in the testing of Fortress (B17) aircraft and the B19. I remember having my first view of the great lakes and the Canadian border during these tests. During the visit we met several members of the BAC staff and we were to see them quite a lot in the coming weeks. Between 1 and 9 June I made three trips between Washington and Dayton giving presentations and attending conferences and meetings. On 11 June I was off again to Norfolk in Virginia and the airbase in Langley Field. Hearsum and I flew down after lunch and, for once, had been booked into a very poor hotel. Norfolk was very full of visitors with a number of large conventions and military exercises. We had to share a room and sleep was almost impossible. The heat and humidity were exceptionally high and although there was a huge fan in the centre of the ceiling with a three foot long blade, its bearings were so noisy that sleep was impossible either because the fan was switched off and we were too hot or it was on and the noise was quite deafening. Fortunately when our contact from Langley came to collect us next morning he very quickly fixed us up with rooms in the Officers' Club and all was well. We spent five days at Langley and flew several ASV test sorties out into the Caribbean in B17s. On one of these trips the aircraft was several hundred miles out to sea over the Caribbean on the way back to Langley and an American crew member was watching the ASV radar when suddenly all hell let loose. Depth charges dropped out one after the other and machine guns at front, rear and central positions on left and right all let go. Meanwhile the aircraft dived towards the sea. It turned out that a German submarine had been sighted and with typical American enthusiasm the whole crew had reacted. Back at Langley there was some attempt to claim a kill and I, having been 'brought up' with RAF Coast Command and their rigorous claim criteria, was somewhat unpopular in pointing out that there were no signs of debris or oil afterwards and such a claim was dubious.

Having completed the task at Langley and determined that the signals team on the base were competent to carry on we planned to return to Washington on 17 June. The team at Langley kindly offered to fly us back to Bolling Field; an Airforce base near the capital city. Again after a session of reporting and planning I set out by air for Dayton on 19 June and on this occasion we concentrated on the final clearance of the B17. This task took us through to a final successful flight test over the Great Lakes on 8 July. At this point I should say what a helpful team the BAC had in Dayton. It was also a happy team under Wing Cdr Cedric Bell with whom, again, I was to have considerable dealings later in my civil service career when he became an Assistant Director of Communications at the Ministry of Technology. Being midsummer there were lots of swimming parties and it was in Dayton that I was first introduced to the traditional Mint Julip, and it became a real favourite with me on these warm summer evenings, together with the croaks of bullfrogs and flashes of fireflies. However, it wasn't always so nice and on one occasion I remember coming out of an air-conditioned cinema at midnight into 95° F and 98% humidity. Quite horrible – rather like walking around in a shower!

It was now time to check up on progress at Consolidated and at Lockheed on the West Coast and on 10 July I left Dayton by air for Los Angeles and by train to San Diego. This last leg of the journey was interesting and extremely comfortable as I travelled on the famous Santa Fe Express and in its Club Car.

Final flight tests on the Catalina involved flying over the Comoro

Islands and down the Gulf of California and the Mexican Coast. The results were very satisfactory and Mr Cooper and the firm's design team had done well so that this would be the last visit to San Diego. Before leaving I made a final visit to the North Island Navy station and in the evening the young officers who had taken me to Tijuana on the previous visit decided on a swimming party on Long Beach – a delightful experience on a beautiful summer evening.

Later, in the afternoon of 14 July I flew to Burbank and checked in at the Hollywood Roosevelt Hotel again. I joined the RTO again early next morning at Lockheed to make the final checks on the Hudson installation.

Lunch that day was unusually interesting and a pleasant surprise. Again – typically American – the Hudson aircraft being supplied to the USAF often had quite clever and colourful cartoon figures painted on the side of the nose. Many, of course, were of gorgeous young women rather like those of the well known calendars. The Disney Studios had been contracted to produce some of these as a morale booster and on this occasion Walt Disney was on site to oversee what his staff were doing. He was already friendly with the RTO and I was introduced and we were invited to lunch with Walt at the Disney Studios. As one might expect he was a very colourful character and we had a most interesting lunch learning some of the basic techniques used to produce his films and cartoons.

Having cleared the Hudson I was on my way back to Dayton that evening and next morning, 16 July, in the BAC offices we planned my trip to Vancouver and Ottawa which would start from Washington on the 23rd. Meanwhile, in the next few days we carried out more work on the B17 aircraft and an unusual type, the B18, with more flying up to the Great Lakes and back. On 20 July I had my last day with the team in Dayton. Wing Commander Cedric Bell and his team had been so helpful and there had been so many enjoyable leisure hour events during my visits that this was rather a sad farewell.

I travelled that night back to Washington on a sleeper on the Ohio State Railway and reported in the next morning to BAC to find that my date for return to the UK had been confirmed for 11 August. However, in the interval I was expected to make one more big journey. I was scheduled to visit the Boeing Aircraft Corporation at Seattle and then on to their Shadow factory – recently opened in Vancouver, Canada, where they were to augment production of PBY Catalina Aircraft under licence to the Consolidated Aircraft Corporation. Thus I was scheduled to depart Washington for Seattle by air on 23 July. After a final session at Wright Patterson Airforce base I left for Washington by train on 21 July and after further reporting and also attending a conference on aircraft electronic equipment standards I left for Seattle via Chicago and Salt Lake City as scheduled with United Airlines.

I had discussions with the appropriate sections of the Boeing design office in Seattle who were to be associated with their company's latest commitment in Vancouver and met a Peter Cook of Canadian Vickers. I then, on the advice previously given me from Dayton, took the famous Greyhound bus to Vancouver, and I was very pleased that I did. The splendour of the Washington State and the Mount Reiner area with the Columbia River providing the border with Canada literally took my breath away. I understand the climate is such that one can swim comfortably at the foot of Mount Reiner most of the year and ski at the top. This part of the USA turned out to be my favourite.

In Vancouver I stayed at the Vancouver Hotel and reported next morning at the Royal Canadian Air Force Headquarters. I met with Wing Commander Norman, one of their senior communications officers, whom I had met previously in the UK when he came to Helensburgh to see what we were doing with the Catalina DP 202. He and I made visits to the new Boeing

'Shadow' factory and had useful exchanges with senior engineering staff regarding airborne radar. I was fortunate while I was in Vancouver to attend the ceremony of the launching of the first Catalinas off their new production line.

During the weekend, with Norman and two other RCAF officers I was given a wonderful tour of this spectacular part of the world. This included a visit to Prospect Point, and the famous redwood trees, including the very big one through the trunk of which it is possible to drive a bus. We also fished for blue trout from a motor launch on Horseshoe Bay. During this expedition moose and buffalo could be seen on some of the tree-covered hills rising from the water of the lake. This first introduction to Canada and Canadians at home was a delightful experience.

After further ASV presentations in the RCAF headquarters I left Vancouver for Ottawa. However, again on the advice of the Dayton team, I travelled by Canadian Pacific Railway from Vancouver to Calgary in Alberta across the Rocky Mountains and through Kicking Horse Pass. The scenery was, of course, quite spectacular and unforgettable. I would not have missed it for anything. Again, thanks to the Dayton BAC team for arranging it.

Arriving in Ottawa I was met by one of our liaison officers and was shepherded into the Chateau Laurier hotel. The very, very European environment was striking in those days. I wonder if it has changed much? Ottawa seemed, on this short visit, to be all parks and scenery and very little industry. I reported in to the RCAF headquarters the next morning. Again, WCdr Norman was there and seemed to be the main officer responsible for the new radar facilities, with large emphasis on coastal and maritime operations. I also met his staff. We had several meetings and I gave the usual ASV presentations.

Once again hospitality was generous and my impression of Canada and the Canadian people could not have been more pleasing.

I left Ottawa on 1 August for Washington by air via Philadelphia. On the journey a surprising thing happened which I believe was more likely to happen in this great country than almost anywhere else in the world. I sat next to an American businessman in the aircraft whose name was Hook and whose home was on the outskirts of Philadelphia. We struck up quite a varied line of conversation and just before landing he suggested I stop over with him, meet his family and stay overnight with them. On the spur of the moment, so to speak, this I did. It could not have been more enjoyable and his wife, his son and his daughter were charming people. I especially remember that in his garden he had an outstanding crop of sweet corn which, of course, at this time of the year, was just ripe and ready to use. The sweet corn, with cobs of butter, made up an important part of the menu at dinner that evening and it was exceptionally good.

I continued on to Washington next morning where in addition to reporting I found I was required again at Consolidated in San Diego as they had met an unexpected problem. It was planned for me to fly down overnight next day on 4 August. Meanwhile, during my short stay in Washington, the head of the American Airlines office in that city arrived at the BAC offices to present me with a framed certificate to say I had been appointed 'Admiral of their Flagship Fleet', having flown over 10,000 miles on civil airlines in America, the majority with American Airlines.

Flying to Los Angeles on this occasion we were due to make a stop at Nashville in Tennessee. Not far from the airport we ran into what still is the worst thunderstorm I have ever experienced in the air. We were flying in cloud descending from about 20 miles out when we must have flown right through the centre (funnel) of the storm. The air was rough in the extreme and the dear old DC3 was 'standing on its ear' at times but – the lightning! This was both frightening and spectacular. The radio was hit and lightning played along the wings and over the fuselage. Off the wing tips there was a continuous performance of St Elmo's Fire for many minutes. We landed at Nashville in the most tremendous downpour that I have ever experienced.

I spent 5 and 6 August at Consolidated at San Diego, during which we cleared a number of problems that had arisen resulting in reduced performance. If I remember rightly, differences in the material used in the aerial systems required some small adjustments to the length of the aerials to return to full resonance.

I returned to Washington on 7 August and spent the next three days at BAC with reporting and farewells all round including the Navy Bureau and the USAF offices. On the 12th I flew to Baltimore and joined the BOAC-operated Clipper to the UK via Botwood and Shannon; an uneventful flight but including a super full Irish / English breakfast in the early morning at Shannon. We eventually landed in Poole harbour and I later rejoined my wife at her parents home in Felixstowe.

TRE Great Malvern

Whilst I was in America the whole TRE establishment had moved yet again and this time to Great Malvern in Worcestershire. Once again this move was part of the nervousness of having such an important defence research unit in a vulnerable site on the South Coast. In February our special forces had raided the German ground radar station at Bruneval on the French channel coast to collect information about their system and it was thought possible that the Germans might 'return the compliment'. Great Malvern is about as far from the coast as one can get in England and it was therefore decided to move the whole of TRE into the buildings of the Malvern Boys College, which was made up of a large ancient main building supported by six or seven large houses all surrounding a sizeable grass lawn. By the time I arrived back from America the whole team had just about settled again and were 'in business', so to speak.

My wife joined me in Malvern and we were fortunate to get accommodation in a pleasant house with a local bank manager and his wife and daughter. Later we were able to occupy a flat in the Malvern House Hotel which had been commandeered by the Government for TRE married staff. This flat had wonderful views to the east across the Vale of Evesham and Bredon Hill.

I found myself back with my previous colleague John Pringle. In general Pringle's 1½ metre airborne radar team occupied House 2 and were just about to start a programme to produce a new air/ground system code named Rebecca/Eureka. This was a radar transmitter/receiver equipment for installation in aircraft and an associated ground transponder beacon equipment (Eureka). Much of the design of Rebecca was borrowed from the basic ASV. 2.

This system was planned to have many applications in situations where aircraft were required to locate, precisely, a position on the ground which was capable of operating a Eureka beacon. Such sites included airfields, dropping zones, friendly vehicles and ships, and some were hidden in the farms and barns belonging to partisans in Europe.

Throughout the next three and a half years I was comparatively stable and based at Malvern but with frequent short periods of outside duty involving headquarters in London and many air force, army and navy establishments on advisory tasks. I will note here that ASV Mk II adaptations were made and deployed on Fleet Air Arm aircraft and on destroyers of the Royal Navy. ASV and Rebecca/Eureka were also manufactured in Australia in quantity and used in their maritime aircraft and ships.

During this period I became involved in the Halifax and the Lysander aircraft at Tempsford airfield near Bedford. The squadrons stationed here were involved in clandestine operations in which partisans in Europe were supplied with equipment, food and transport to and from such nations as Holland, Denmark, Belgium, France etc. In the laboratories we built many special

Eureka equipments camouflaged in, for example, Huntley and Palmer biscuit tins which could be hidden in the attics and barns of the partisans and would be unlikely to draw the attention of the occupying forces. These beacons could be used to assist the air crews to locate the dropping zones or even left purposely close to a target such as a local enemy headquarters or quisling's residence to provide identification of the target and help avoid damage to the locals.

One particular incident at this time I remember well. It will be appreciated that these support services were especially hush-hush, and John Pringle and I went through a period of travelling between Malvern and Tempsford hand delivering the latest equipment and instructing the agents and aircrew as necessary. The timing of these missions was vitally important and John Pringle could be a very determined chap. On one occasion we had had some unsuspected difficulties in completing one of the beacons which was required to be available at a certain time at the Tempsford airfield. Late, we loaded his MG Magnette outside House 2, roared along the school drive to the main gate which, fortunately, was open. At that moment, John shouted, "Damn, I've forgotten the authorization pass for the equipment!" Whereupon he put his foot on the accelerator and we rushed past the guards, one of whom fired at our tyres with his revolver, but fortunately missed. The equipment was delivered on time but the fury of the Superintendent who called us into his office on return next day can be imagined. He certainly did not accept that the result justified the deed!

During these years 1943, 1944 and 1945 I was comparatively settled in Malvern with my wife for the first time since we married, and the work at TRE on Rebecca / Eureka systems, which we had developed, progressed into quantity production with companies such as Pye Radio Ltd of Cambridge and Murphy Radio of Welwyn Garden City. However, we still were involved in making some of the special beacons for use in occupied Europe with our own fair hands. This work also involved training sessions for those volunteers from Europe who were to use them 'back home', so to speak. As one might expect these courageous people were intelligent and thoughtful and made excellent students. However, one rather unusual outcome is worth recording. This occurred a month or so before the planned invasion of the North African coast. An American landing party was to be put ashore from a submarine a few days before and it was planned for a small party of Americans to come to Malvern for the usual instruction course on the Eureka beacon which would be used to mark the dropping zones for the following parachutists. Surprise was expressed by all of us on the arrival of three of the most obvious gum chewing GIs one can imagine. However, they completed the course and were due to make the final check. It was normal to send those involved from House 2 in the dark across to the other side to the TRE site. They would then set up the beacon, send a coded pulse message back to the Rebecca equipment in House 2, receive and decode the response and return to House 2. This exercise was completed without any difficulty by the GIs and we were awaiting their return in a laboratory on the first floor when there was a sudden racket in the lobby downstairs. One of our GIs had tripped over the step as he entered carrying the Eureka which rolled about fifteen yards across the lobby floor with a great clatter! We were not surprised to hear later that, having been put ashore in North Africa as planned, they were discovered and made prisoners almost immediately. Fortunately they were able to detonate the explosive charges in each beacon to avoid them being used by the enemy to mark false dropping zones.

At this time the special teams at Tempsford were asking if it was possible to improve the accuracy of approach to the dropping zones when delivering to the partisans in Europe. Our first attempt to achieve this objective was to design a special aerial on the delivery

23. Rebecca Precision Homing Aerials on Halifax

Halifax aircraft so that the pilots could run up to the Eureka radar ground marker beacon with more precision. This aerial was made up of two multi-element Yagi arrays mounted under the nose with their narrow beams cutting sharply across each other thus producing a very sharply defined cross over of the two beams which were produced. This resulted in a considerable improvement in the operations (Fig 23).

During late 1944 we received a further request, this time from those responsible for Airborne Forces, to consider whether the Eureka beacon could be improved to provide more accurate approach to the dropping zones than the standard equipment which only marked a point on the ground allowing an aircraft equipped with Rebecca to home to the point. What was wanted, particularly in cases of a very confined dropping zone, was an approach 'beam' to assist the aircraft to approach along a specific path predetermined by the ground operators such as advanced forces and partisans.

We started a research programme on this and I little realized at the time how this work would have a major bearing on my future career, particularly after the war. At this time our experimental flying was carried out at the aerodrome at Defford in the Vale of Evesham. It had one of the Standard HF Beam Approach systems (SBA) on the main runway, which was being installed at a large number of RAF airfields. It was installed on the centre line of the main runway at the upwind end and some distance out towards the boundary and at such a distance that it would cause no serious obstruction to aircraft approaching from that end. We were also aware of an American system SCS 51 on VHF frequencies which provided a similar but more precise service. They both provided overlapping beams such that the crossover, where their signals were equal, defined the line of approach to the runway. The two beams carried different coded signals so that aircraft going off to right or left received more of one code than the other. Thus, flying to keep the signals equal, the aircraft approached the runway along the centre line. A number of vertical marker beacons provided a crude idea of the distance from touchdown. However, both systems were far too large to move around as a system for advance forces and special operations.

Whilst we were developing our early ideas to satisfy the requirement, it just so happened that one of the university professors who had been drafted into TRE circulated a treatise on slot aerials in which the familiar 1½ metre dipole aerials could be replaced by a resonant cavity with a slot cut in it having similar dimensions to the equivalent dipole. This made our job much easier and, to cut a long story short, we built a cavity as a cube of dimensions meeting the requirements for resonance and cut a 'dipole' slot around the front and side of each front corner. A probe in the centre of the cavity fed energy into it and the slots were

-B.A.B.S. Mk. II, showing aerial system.

(a)

(b)

(a) Equisignal path.

(b) Aircraft 5° to starboard.

24. Radar Beam Approach System (BABS)

shorted alternately by relays operating across the middle of each slot. The cavity was placed appropriately in a horn aerial to determine the beam coverage pattern required. Thus we produced the necessary overlapping beams and, in this case, being radar, the signal provided the displacement information about the centre line but in addition provided a continuous reading of range to the runway. We named this system BABS – (Beam Approach Beacon System) (Fig 24).

The reader will appreciate from the figure how this arrangement was convenient for installation in a standard RAF type DRLS van which allowed the wings of the horn aerial to be folded for transit. The early development model was made with the expert assistance of the TRE workshop and trials at Defford were very successful. Thus, a contract was placed on Pye Radio Ltd of Cambridge for production. The first one from the Pye production was involved later in a demonstration and proving trial at a wartime airfield at Bottisham near Cambridge. This demonstration was attended by senior officers from the Air Ministry, Airborne Forces, the Parachute Regiment, etc. and was remarkably successful! It was arranged for a Halifax aircraft from Tempsford to mount a resupply operation using the BABS beam. Thus the vehicle was run into position, the horn aerial opened out and the facility switched on just as the aircraft was heard on the horizon. On the first run-in the 2lb bag of white flour landed within ten yards of the BABS. The second run was even more accurate, so much so that it was also a small disaster! The 2lb bag which was quite a missile at the speed it arrived, went straight into the horn aerial of the BABS and completely wrecked the resonant cavity and feeding system. The equipment had to be returned to the factory for a major repair. What price success?

During this period the Rebecca, Eureka, and BABS programmes now continued to be delivered to various RAF and Army units requiring this type of operational assistance, firstly in Europe and later in the Far East. However, just as work was, for me, beginning to get a little monotonous, (in R&D terms) a new activity developed which, again, was to have a large impact on my future career. At Defford an American officer, one Col Moseley, influenced his seniors to allocate one of their military versions of the ILS (Instrument Landing System) beam system to Defford, and, as a close friend of the Commanding Officer, Gp Capt McDonald, he set up an ad hoc experiment to get some experience in automatic approach to a runway. Moseley was able to use an old American Boeing two engine airliner which was one of the few aircraft in those days which had an early automatic pilot installation (Fig 25). Of course, this work was not official and not on the TRE list of budgeted projects and activities. However, since it became the Gp Captain's pet it proceeded and I helped a Squadron Leader

25. Boeing Airliner Type 347 with Auto Approach

Griffiths, a Flt Lt Barber and Col Moseley with bits and pieces from my laboratory in House 2 to construct what today would probably be called a modem and which we called a coupling unit, to convert the ILS and BABS signals into a form which would operate the automatic pilot circuits.

After clearing a few problems and generally fine tuning the system the aircraft was able to make very good automatic approaches down to about 200 foot using the ILS localizer and glide path beams. It was not long before we had demonstrated it to senior staff at TRE, to our colleagues in the autopilot design team at RAE Farnborough and to senior officers in both the Ministry of Aircraft Production and the Air Ministry. This 'private enterprise' project occupied the period up to the end of the war in Europe in May 1995. At this point a great deal of effort involving Rebecca and Eureka switched to the continuing war with the

Japanese in the Far East. Meanwhile, in the UK, a great deal of attention was switched to planning and implementing programmes aimed at putting the country into a good position to 'win the peace'. Very soon everyone concerned was convinced that we should set up a special system team to achieve the full automatic landing of aircraft. The main justification at the time was the vulnerability of the RAF 'V' Bombers if caught on the ground due to bad visibility, say, in a November fog. The plan wisely involved setting up a team with experience of aerodynamics, radio and radar navigation and guidance, with automatic pilot development and with recording and aircraft trials expertise. This, I believe was one of the first total system teams to be set up with special facilities including the use of one of the wartime emergency landing strips. The latter were very long and wide and would allow margins for safety in this early aircraft experiment in flying down to ground under automatic control. The airstrip chosen was at Woodbridge in Suffolk and the site chosen for all the operational support for aircraft and research facilities was to be at RAF Martlesham Heath, within a few miles of the Woodbridge emergency strip. I immediately became very interested in this plan because, as very much an East Anglian, I saw a chance to return to this delightful part of England.

Chapter 6

Automatic Landing Research

Towards the end of 1945, with both the European and the Japanese wars over, the plans to set up the Blind Landing Experimental Unit (BLEU) at Martlesham Heath airfield in Suffolk moved swiftly. The first contingent was housed in temporary accommodation on the Woodbridge emergency airstrip in early 1946, whilst the accommodation and the supporting facilities were being prepared at Martlesham Heath RAF Airfield nearby. Meanwhile, it had been decided that I would move to Martlesham later in 1946 as Head of the Guidance Team. Just before this move was scheduled my wife presented us with a daughter, Judith, and we moved as a family in the late spring to Felixstowe again. After a short period with my wife's family, we settled into a very nice flat in the Marlborough Hotel on the front overlooking the North Sea. This was but a few miles from Martlesham and we were back amongst relatives and all our old friends in Felixstowe and with a sailing boat on the beach in front of the flat.

Initially the BLEU programme was aimed to ensure the new V Bombers would not be sitting targets in a November fog, unable to take off because these very expensive aircraft would not be able to land back safely in such conditions. Later the priority was switched to deal with civil airliners. The Superintendent of the new BLEU was a Mr Pritchard from the Instrument and Photographic Department of the RAE at Farnborough. During my time at BLEU Martlesham Heath – about 10 years – Superintendent Pritchard was succeeded in turn by Gerald Touch, Bill Mackinson and John Charnley – later Sir John. The complete BLEU team under

26. Automatic Landing the BLEU Team

John Charnley is shown in Fig 26. My team was a mixture of radio, radar, and communications experts from both TRE and RAE and we started by installing the localizer beam facilities at Woodbridge (Fig 27). A fixed version of BABS and a UK version of the American Instrument Landing Systems (ILS), both produced by Pye Radio Ltd, were soon ready and the operational team started to make approaches using Devon, Varsity and Lancaster aircraft fitted with early automatic pilots. These early flights were using the two systems at the upwind end of the runway for guidance in the horizontal plane and the glide path at 3° was defined by similar systems but with overlapping beams in the vertical plane located at the downwind end of the runway. The localizers were sited in line with the runway and located about one hundred yards into the overshoot area. The glide path equipment was off to one side of the runway opposite the nominal point of touchdown.

We began our work using both the systems. However, in order to ensure an organized expansion of world civil aviation, it was decided at United Nations level to set up a UN organization for the purpose of defining requirements. Initially this was known as the Provisional International Civil Aviation Organization (PICAO). Later the Provisional was dropped and ICAO became the basis for

27. BLEU Systems Guidance Team

setting rules and regulations on all aspects of civil flying including all weather landing and it still has this role.

Although we, the UK, put forward BABS as the standard for approach guidance to airports because it also provided ranges to the runway, the Americans were successful in getting their ILS chosen, not the least since they had many equivalent military SCS 51 equipments surplus from the war and had generously presented them to many of the less affluent nations. However, looking back, I think it was the right choice and it is still the standard. Thus, we decided not to proceed with BABS.

Unfortunately the PYE built UK version of ILS did not use the Alford loop aerials of the American system but produced the beams using what is known as a Sturba array. This aerial is very sensitive to phase changes resulting in the beam moving about the centre line. When this was realized, naturally any poor performance in the overall ground/air automatic landing system was blamed on the azimuth guidance signal. These complaints from the automatic pilot team resulted in two major developments in guidance. Firstly we developed a system in which two wires were laid, one on each side of the runway and out into the approach. Each carried a different modulation frequency around 1000 cycles. A rotating loop aerial under the aircraft detected these two signals independently of attitude. These signals were set to be equal along the centre line of the approach and one or other predominated as the aircraft moved off to either side of the centre line. This system was named 'Leader Cables' and was capable of great accuracy and stability. The runway centre line was defined to an accuracy of 5 feet. From that time, the guidance team received few complaints and the errors in the automatic pilot and in the aerodynamics of the operation became more clearly defined and of more concern. As a highly accurate reference system indicating the displacement from centre of the Woodbridge runway in its electrically quiet environment this was ideal but, unfortunately, it would have been impractical in a normal civil airport environment. Its signal could be transferred by induction into other adjacent circuits such as, for example, those of the runway and the general lighting circuits, which did not necessarily remain in line with the runway. These circuits could carry a distorting signal almost anywhere and caused interference and bends on the approach. For instance, housing estates on the edge of a city airport in the approach area could play havoc with the guidance. However, Leader Cables provided us with an important and very accurate reference system for approach and runway guidance for experimental testing, even though there was no question of it being put forward as an operational system.

The second development stemming from the problem of instability of the early Pye ILS system was a new aerial for the UK version of ILS developed in the first place by my team at Martlesham. We built a parabolic shaped frame or mirror at the nominal ILS frequency using poles from the local Forestry Commission and horizontal wires were draped around the pole framework. These wires were at sufficiently close intervals in the vertical that, at the VHF frequency, the parabolic mirror 'looked' virtually solid. Two stands carrying dipoles were placed offset about the focal point and when energized by a transmitter, produced the necessary overlapping beams. This system proved to be very stable and was made in a production version using metal poles, etc, by Pye Radio Ltd. These, later, were installed and operated on a large number of our RAF airfields.

Now that my small Guidance Team had rid themselves of all the immediate work associated with horizontal guidance systems, we set about considering how to tackle the problem of vertical guidance in the final landing phase after leaving the glide path beam. However, one story is worth a mention before leaving this section. One morning an official of the Post Office arrived in the Superintendent's office to complain that the main telephone cable across the North Sea had been suffering from severe interference over the last several weeks. This had been traced to our leader cable which we had on several occasions unknowingly laid on top of their buried cable for several hundreds of yards. Their customers had to speak above a strong 1000 cycle note. Fortunately this was soon dealt with by moving our cables only a very small distance to one side, since induced energy falls off rapidly with separation distance. We had one other problem in maintaining the leader cable signal, which would mysteriously cut out from time to time. The lack of continuity of service was traced to a local scrap dealer who, on several occasions, had helped himself to a hundred yards of this cable which he found in the woods!

The work to devise a guidance system for the final approach and flare-out on to the runway led us to consider a number of possibilities. We did some tests on the conventional radio altimeter of the time which was using frequency modulation techniques, but these were not able to work below about 20 feet. We also examined an established pulse radar system, but again the minimum operating height was dictated by the smallest pulse width which was practical at the time and again was far too long. On examining the frequency modulated type further it seemed that, if we could use a much higher carrier frequency and thus be able to sweep the modulation over a wider band, we might provide a solution down to one or two feet.

With the assistance of the BLEU workshop we machined a cavity with a resonance at around 4000 megahertz into which the anode plate of a small transmitter valve protruded. A small ceramic shaft was introduced through a hole in the cavity side which had a thin flat section at its end. This flat section was silver plated on either side and the shaft was rotated above the anode plate at a frequency of about 1000 cycles and above the 'flicker' frequency. After several experiments we were able to sweep the 4,000 Mhz basic signal up and down over 100 Mhz and still maintain a reasonably constant output. This signal was fed into a small horn aerial which shared a common base plate with a similar horn aerial for receiving which fitted up into the underbelly of the aircraft. Flight tests in the Anson aircraft were successful and an accurate measurement of height was obtained right down to wheels touching the runway. A minimum aerial height was about 2ft. Fortuitously on one occasion I was given an opportunity to observe this altimeter performance below this height when the pilot, after a number of landings, completely forgot to lower the undercarriage for landing. My first thoughts, as the altimeter was starting to indicate below the set ground zero which represented the height from the belly of the aircraft to the ground, were that my new altimeter was faulty and the zero had changed. Then there was a loud crunching sound of ripping metal, both propellers hit the ground, the engines stopped abruptly and we came to a shuddering halt. Fortunately neither I nor the pilot was hurt but the latter suffered a very severe shock to his pride (Fig 28).

After the success with our measurement of height we then de-

28. The Special Landing Altimeter was correct!

veloped a small computer which differentiated height against time with suitable constants to zero which in effect produced an exponential path for flaring out to the runway surface. This approximated the exponential path which a pilot would use normally on a good landing. All this development required a very large number of test runs in the course of perfecting the performance. Because flying was expensive and not the best environment for making adjustments etc. we devised an entirely practical test arrangement. We mounted the twin horns in a base plate in the vertical plane on the front of a Fordson vehicle and drove it forward and backwards to and from the front of the very large metal doors of the large bomber hangar which was at Martlesham Heath at that time – now the site of a Tesco store – this simulated very well the performance of our flareout guidance and in addition to saving expensive flying also facilitated easier experimentation.

The arrangement also led to a rather amusing incident. We had been using this test method for two or three months when an officer from the Civil Service Fraud Investigation department presented himself in my office/laboratory one morning. We had used some 50 gallons of petrol in a period and only a few tens of miles had been run, according to the mileometer on the Fordson vehicle. Imagine how deflated the chap became when the truth was revealed. The vehicle had a unique mileometer which clocked up mileage running forward and wiped it off if the vehicle reversed. Our test involved constantly running up to the hangar door and backing away again! Hence the only mileage recorded was that in running from the vehicle park and back before and after the experiments. Still, it was comforting, as a tax payer, to know that our civil service is so vigilant!

The flare-out guidance system was applied to the automatic control of the Devon aircraft, and was soon producing very nice, if rather positive landings using the exponential flare. The reason for the rather positive arrival was the need to aim to land, effectively, about two feet below the runway surface otherwise, if all the limits involved happened to be on the negative side, the aircraft would, theoretically, never reach the ground but could fly on up the runway at a tangent to the surface.

Clearly a human pilot, at his best, can 'grease' an aircraft on to the runway and equally he can drop it in at several feet per second rate of descent if he has indigestion or has had a row with his wife! The autolanding is very consistent and set at about 2 or 3 feet per second rate of descent at touchdown. This is often described as rather positive.

This landing guidance system that we developed was to become an internationally adopted one and is still, I believe, the basic system in use in civil aviation.

It is interesting to record that in the early 1950s the American All Weather Team flew a DC4 from Kennedy airport to Bovingdon in the UK under automatic control from take off to landing.

However, the landing was very heavy because the aircraft flew the ILS glide path at 3° straight to touchdown with no flare-out.

This first in aviation by the USA was heralded in the press, quite rightly. However, two days later the DC4 flew to visit BLEU at Martlesham to give demonstrations and to exchange ideas on the all weather landing problems. It is significant that they were not prepared to make totally automatic landings but only low approaches. Clearly they had risked the undercarriage in a very hard landing in order to register a 'first'. During their visit we demonstrated our automatic approach and flared landing system and they were very impressed with our flare out right down to the ground. Later in the visit arrangements were made for us to make a flare-out equipment for their DC4 aircraft.

When the equipment was ready I was invited to Dayton in Ohio to advise on the installation and testing. As a part of this assignment, the Ministry headquarters decided the equipment and test gear would need to be sent to America by special freight aboard ship. The ship chosen was the Cunard Liner *Queen Mary*. It was also decided that I would travel on the same sailing and be responsible for the equipment's arrival on board, to check it each day and to hand it over to a Ministry representative in New York. He would then have the responsibility to ensure its safe arrival at the All Weather Unit near Dayton, Ohio.

For me this was a wonderful experience. I travelled in Cabin Class in comparative luxury. For the first time I saw dolphins playing in front of the bow of the ship. Beautiful creatures in their own element. The voyage was uneventful except for a 12-hour storm described as a 'rough whole gale' the third day out. The North West Atlantic was impressive in this state and in a forty knot gale the ship, big as it was, heaved and slammed about and had to drop down to five knots for a while. However, we docked in New York next morning and I handed over my charge.

There was a sequel to this. On arrival at Dayton two days later, after reporting to the Embassy in Washington, the valuable freight was nowhere to be seen. After much hiatus it was traced over on the west coast in Los Angeles and brought back by express air freight. So much for the security! We were then able to start the programme on the C54 aircraft. This went smoothly and gave a very good flare-out performance and, as usual, my American friends of the All Weather Flight decided on a celebration. Thus once again I found myself having dinner in the Flagship restaurant in Dayton and staying in the Officers' Club at Wright-Patterson Airforce Base near Dayton. I arrived late in the evening after an excellent dinner and my room was impossibly hot so I decided to open a window. This was a bigger task than I had anticipated because clearly it had not been opened for a very long time, if ever! However I finally won the battle over the rust with a nail file and settled down to sleep in comparative comfort. About midnight I was conscious of a great commotion in the corridor outside but dismissed this as some officers returning from Dayton after an evening out. A black steward arriving with some tea in the morning exploded on entering my room. "Gee you are the one who has blown up my boiler during the night. It has been trying to hold the set temperature and the heat is all escaping out of your window and I am getting complaints about the cold." So much for the appreciation of fresh air!

During my stay I had another interesting experience early one very nice morning when I decided to walk from the Club down the road to a typical American 'Diner' for breakfast – a distance of about one mile. I had walked only some 200 yards when a large police car pulled up beside me and a large policeman shouted "Where the hell do you think you are going?" When I said I was walking to the diner for breakfast his reply was "Like hell you are! Get in the car and I'll take you." On the way, he explained that it was illegal to walk on the highway. On leaving me he remarked "Hell, of course you had to be English!" Whilst on this visit I built up a friendship with Col Taylor, head of their All Weather team and Jim Anast, his top research and development engineer. Jim was married to a very beautiful French girl, but what went wrong with his life I cannot imagine. His career seemed to be successful and he, at one stage, was a technical advisor in the White House. Jim took his own life; such a waste of talent and such a nice bright chap.

It is worth recounting another story associated with our flare out development. At one stage in the programme BLEU mounted a presentation of our work. This event involved several live demonstrations both on the ground and in the air. One ground demonstration involved our flare-out system. This took the form of a rather basic aircraft cockpit with an indicator which, when its needle pointer was horizontal, was at zero. This, through the flare-out computer, would remain on zero whilst the 'aircraft' was flying on the exponential path to the runway during the final 100ft. It would indicate up or down by an amount depending on how far off the exponential flare path the 'aircraft' was flying. In other words, flying to hold the indicator at zero ensured a correctly flared landing. Many visitors 'flew' the aircraft and were suitably impressed. There came the occasion when the Director of RAE, our top boss, opted to have a go! He did very well and made an excellent landing but at the critical moment of 'touchdown' a colleague standing behind him dropped an empty biscuit tin with a great clatter directly behind him. The great man took it very well, but to say he 'jumped out of his skin' fairly describes it. The technical assistant who perpetrated this 'joke' was true to type and never one to hold back from what he considered to be a great opportunity.

During this period at BLEU my team was involved in three other interesting research studies which are worthy of short descriptions for the record. One, called the 'Televiewer' project, was aimed to establish the possibility of using high frequency low power radiobeacons as point sources set out along the runway edge much as are the normal optical lights. However, whereas with thick fog the normal lighting is obscured it seemed possible that a suitable radio frequency might be selected which could combine penetration with still sufficient definition to mark a point source to indicate the runway on the cathode ray tube picture in the aircraft.

Before starting work on the radio beacons we decided to examine the practicality of a pilot's ability to land safely viewing a television picture. This we simulated by installing a television type camera in the nose of an NF11 twin seat Meteor aircraft. The pilot in the front position viewed the picture on the screen through a visor. This was partly in order to keep out extraneous light but more importantly to fix the distance between the retina and the tube face. The tests were carried out in the dark using the normal visual lighting pattern We established that landing was practical provided one or two important criteria were satisfied. The most important was to fix the distance between the retina and the tube face so that the image on the retina was projected at infinity and on a scale of 1:1 compared to normal sight. Differences of scale factor produced serious errors of judgement. The pilots also needed to be able to adjust contrast and brilliance to suit their own eyesight characteristics. Having decided that 'blind landings' were possible, I cannot remember why we did not proceed to produce a system. Perhaps because the actual fog landing trials were indicating that, even in thick fog, it was still possible for a pilot to see sufficient of the normal landing pattern of lights to determine if it is safe for the automatic landing to be completed or to initiate an automatic overshoot if at low height the pilot is not satisfied. I seem to remember this work was at this stage when the move to Bedford disrupted the flow of development and since I did not go to Bedford on this occasion I do not recall what happened to this project but I don't think it went much further.

Another interesting experience during this work at BLEU

concerned the Fleet Air Arm and aircraft carrier landing. We were asked to consider whether any work we were doing on land aircraft could assist with the difficult operation of landing fast jet aircraft on the deck of a carrier. Since we had no knowledge of the problem, I and a colleague were invited to visit the *Pretoria Castle* – a converted merchantman – to get some first hand experience of the operation. Firstly we spent some time in the scuppers opposite the touchdown area. After we had got brave enough to stand up and look – the aircraft always appeared about to be landing on top of us – we watched the 'bat' man aiding the pilot's judgement and the picking up of the arresting wires with the tail hook. I also took part in one or two circuits and landings, which was an exciting experience to say the least. There was some consideration whether the radio altimeter might assist in the approach to the stern of the ship, but the precise height above the sea, which it could offer, was not much assistance in relation to a pitching and rolling deck.

At one stage we, in liaison with British European Airways, also did a little work examining the landing of helicopters in low visibility. This was in the period when they were getting involved in operations to support the north sea oil platforms. In considering and planning the programme we were led to believe that, unlike fixed wing aircraft, the helicopter would require a glide path much higher than 3° and more approaching the vertical. Thus we decided to make some checks with a theodolite, having arranged for the pilot to perform the approach and landing as he would in bad visibility. All were surprised to find that the average angle of approach was around 7°. The reason for this unexpected result – "everyone knows a helicopter lands at near the vertical" – was that in poor visibility there is a need to maintain a certain forward speed in order to ensure the rotor will go into auto-rotation in the event of an engine failure. We, of course, were considering the single engine aircraft. I imagine a twin engine twin rotor aircraft could be quite different.

After the first two or three years at BLEU when the guidance team were devising the various new systems described earlier, we settled down to the job of liaising with Industry, to prepare the necessary specifications and engineering designs for the guidance equipments and getting them made as acceptable prototypes and then into production.

The main companies concerned were Pye Radio Ltd for the parabolic aerial ILS, STC Radio Division for the Flare-out Altimeter, Elliott Automation and Smith Aviation for the automatic pilots and coupling units. Also during this period the team at BLEU were using several different aircraft fitted with early autoland including the Devon, Varsity, Lancaster and BAC 1–11.

A great deal of theoretical work was carried out with the help of the mathematical department in RAE in order to arrive at the level of safety which was required of any system upon which the lives of civil passengers would be totally dependent. After much hard work and considerable controversy a figure of not more than one failure in ten million landings (1 in 10^7) was reached.

A great deal of effort was then devoted to gathering data on as many automatic landings as possible in order to have a sufficient sample to establish that the target had been satisfied. BLEU also learned the psychological need to express the target aim as 'no accident in ten million landings'. In the later periods of my ten years at BLEU (1946–1956) the whole team concentrated on two main tasks. One was to establish the practicality of automatic landing in real fog conditions firstly at Woodbridge and later at London airport. The other was to build up in UK, and later in ICAO, the necessary regulations and specifications to govern this operation in world civil aviation.

In order to gain experience in the real environment, arrangements were made to make full use of any sufficiently low visibility conditions which might occur. A special team from within

BLEU and including our RAF pilots, was set up with quite elaborate arrangements for 'call-out' at any time.

This was very effective. After many operations of this kind using the Woodbridge airstrip we obtained permission to fly into London Heathrow Airport whenever it was closed to other aircraft because visibility was below limits for normal civil flying. The BLEU Devon and Varsity aircraft carried out a number of such sorties which contributed a great deal to the acceptance of the operation later by the civil aviation community as a whole.

One somewhat amusing incident is worth a mention here. The BLEU Varsity was on one of its early sorties to Heathrow on a very foggy morning. It had already made some successful touchdowns and was on another approach at very low height and just in view of the touchdown zone lighting when the pilot found himself presented with a cyclist crossing his path on the perimeter track and he had to initiate an overshoot. When the incident was investigated by the Heathrow Control it turned out a lady cleaner had been identified as the 'culprit'. She said "everybody knows that aircraft don't fly into Heathrow in this weather and I take a short cut on the way home"!

I was not directly involved in the special Fog Team but I did have one or two trips with them for experience.

It is interesting to note that although BLEU had shown that full automatic blind landing was operationally safe and acceptable, it has since been realized that on practically all occasions the pilot would be able see sufficient of the special lighting in the touchdown zone to operate an automatic overshoot if he was not happy with the lateral position and the height of his aircraft at that point. This human opportunity to determine that the landing was safe to proceed was made possible by the very effective new lighting patterns in the approach and touchdown area named 'Calvert Lighting' after the original designer from the RAE, Farnborough.

The other main task in these later stages at Martlesham Heath was building up and defining the basis of an international agreement in ICAO which would set the specification and limits and the regulations for Automatic landings in civil aircraft world wide. For me, personally, this was the start of much liaison work in ICAO in Montreal over several years. The ICAO set up an All Weather Operations Panel and I became its first Chairman, but more of this later.

During this period I became involved in an unexpected project which resulted in visits to Sweden every quarter over two years. The Air Ministry became aware of an approach guidance system being developed by Swedish Philips for the KFF (Swedish Airforce). This was intended for use in their new Viggan fighter aircraft, and there was interest in the RAF since it could have application in the RAF's new Hunter aircraft. Being an approach guidance system my team at BLEU was asked to assess its performance and applicability. The KFF officer responsible, one Torsten Bergens, had good English and turned out to be a very competent and very likeable character. In the two years or so that we were involved in this project he and I became great friends and stayed in each other's homes on various visits. The equipment was code named BARBRO and was a radar guidance system inspired by our own BABS development. The team set up to manage this UK exploratory project consisted of the representative of the KFF, the Swedish Philips Company, the RAF, the Ministry of Technology and BLEU. As head of guidance at BLEU I was given the job of heading up this team.

On the first visit the UK team travelled to Stockholm on the Swedish Lloyd North Sea ferry from Tilbury to Gothenberg and then by rail across Sweden. We left Tilbury at midday on Sunday in the SS *Patricia* and were almost immediately introduced to the smorgasbord of all times for lunch. I cannot properly describe it except to say that it seemed to have some of everything. There were four such ships used on this regular daily service.

The KFF had arranged for us to stay in a special hotel south of Stockholm, the Bads Hotel, at Saltsjöbaden, which was a cross between an hotel and a nursing home but the very limit of comfort and service. At the first meeting in Swedish Philips I was asked to chair the discussion, which involved presentation of the system by Philips and discussions on the programme. The following day we were taken by road to the KFF airbase at Vasteros on Lake Malaren to have some demonstration flights and to inspect the BARBRO prototype ground equipment. The aircraft used for the demonstration was a Fieseler Storch. This was a high wing two or three seat monoplane which, given a little help from the wind could almost stand still in the air. An ideal aircraft for careful examination of an approach beam. The pilot was a delightful character who hailed from Riga. He was an excellent pilot and always ready for a leg pull. I was quite impressed with our first approach but on the third run in I thought I detected a bend in the beam about two miles from the main runway which is approached over the lake. When I mentioned this to the pilot he sounded incredulous and requested that I alert him on the next approach as soon as I started to detect the bend. As we got to the position on this next approach I alerted him as the heading started to move off the true course to the runway. A few seconds later he told me to look over the side and there, about one hundred feet below us, was an island over which we were passing and a large number of naked women lying stretched out sunbathing. "There," he said. "We always have a beam bend over Elba!" The small island was a female nudist club (Fig 29).

There followed a number of progress meetings and then we were ready to approve the prototype. For this visit we had two pilots from the Centre Fighter Establishment at West Raynham who joined us at Vasteros with their Meteor aircraft. The two pilots could not have been more different in character. One had almost the attitude of a university Don and the other gave the appearance

29. BARBRO Beam Bend over Elba!

of a 'devil may care' outlook and all the world was fun. They tossed up who would make the first test flight and the 'happy go lucky' one went first. In spite of mountainous terrain and a murky morning with the cloud base at only five hundred feet the aircraft roared in on several approaches perfectly aligned with the runway. Arriving at the apron, where we were all awaiting his assessment, he leapt out with a great smile and "it's the best thing since cut bread". The other pilot then took off flying all around under the cloud base and establishing that the beam was giving no incorrect guidance. He then proceeded to carry out his assessment runs. Between them they were well satisfied and BARBRO got approval and a contract was signed.

That evening, Swedish Philip invited all involved to a dinner in the Grand Hotel in Stockholm where they had hired a private suite. On arrival guests were invited into an ante room for the traditional Schnapps with a larger chaser together with what can best be described as 'rotten fish' on little fingers of toast – quite an acquired taste and a driver to another Schnapps. Not surprisingly this produced a very lively party atmosphere. We were then marshalled into the dining room which was very impressive with a very large long table of inlaid mahogany, linen table mats together with silver and a set of the beautiful Orifos glasses made in Sweden. Place names ensured we were well mixed and this dinner was unusual as a business dinner in that all the Swedish wives were present. After a welcoming toast by the Chairman of Swedish Philips we started on the first course – a delicate lobster crêpe. Our jaunty pilot from Raynham was sitting almost opposite me and suddenly disgorged a large set of false teeth which clattered down on the beautiful mahogany table which he gathered up in a very inelegant manner and literally stuffed them back in his mouth. There was a stunned silence and just for a split second I and, I think, practically everyone else felt embarrassed and very sorry for him. It was only when there was a repeat performance that some of us realized this was an RAF dining-in night joke from London's Lyle Street. In some defence for the poor chap he had had too much drink and like all of us, was unused to schnapps. However, the Swedes, who are not noted for humour, could not see this as a joke and we British were terribly embarrassed.

A much more pleasant memory for me was an invitation to sail with the Philips Director in his 'Dragon' yacht in the Swedish Skerries the next day. I found this a little scary at times since, although there were no tides to worry about, the many small islands of lava rock presented me with a lea shore to worry about almost continuously. Nevertheless it was a most enjoyable day. During the two years I experienced Sweden in all its seasonable changes including a crefta party (freshwater crayfish) in the country outside Stockholm on mid-summer's eve which went on all night, although the light was such that the fact that it was the middle of the night was not apparent.

I enjoyed Sweden and learned to like the Swedish people. They were always a little stiff to begin with but once they had got to know you they were some of the most sincere friends and very dependable. Doing business with them verged on the pedantic at times but having undertaken a commitment one could guarantee it would be met to the letter.

In 1956 the RAE, the parent establishment of BLEU, decided to move the whole unit to Thurleigh Airfield in Bedfordshire. So far as the overall programme of development of blind landing and all weather operations was concerned this was a most important move forward.

At Thurleigh the main runway was large and wide with a clear and excellent approach. It was planned to install all the other aids so that development could proceed based on a total system concept.

However, interesting as this programme was, as a true East Anglian I did not look forward to this move one little bit and was looking around for other possible postings. Fortunately at this time a special operation had been set up at Martlesham Heath involving a Vulcan 'V' bomber aircraft and connected with the Atomic Weapon Research Establishment at Aldermaston. This was associated with preparation for the atom bomb trials at Christmas

Island – very hush-hush! The Head of AWRE Trials Department, one Dr Ewan Maddock, was lunching in the Officers' Mess one day and, although I did not know him then, he overheard me saying "I don't want to go to Bedford – it's all bloody brick dust and cabbages!" About a couple of weeks later an advertisement appeared in the *East Anglian Daily Times* for a post as Superintendent in Charge of the AWRE Trials Unit at Orfordness. I learned later that it was deliberately aimed at me and, not surprisingly, I applied and, at an interview at Aldermaston with Dr Maddock and with Dr Penny, the Head of AWRE, I was offered the job. The only snag was that I would be demoted from Senior Principal Scientific Officer to Principal Scientific Officer, with the consequent drop in salary. This turned out to be the second time I accepted demotion to please my personal aspirations. Readers will remember my acceptance of the job at Bawdsey Research Station against my uncle's advice.

However, once again, looking back, I do not regret the move, although in the end I must admit I was very fortunate to be able to say this as my developing career moved on. AWRE seemed to like me and I was reinstated to Senior Principal Scientific Officer quite quickly after settling down as Superintendent and Officer-in-Charge of AWRE Orfordness.

Just before leaving BLEU in 1959 I was awarded the Wakefield Gold Medal of the Royal Aeronautical Society for my work on Blind Landing Systems.

Chapter 7

Atomic Weapon Research – Orfordness

I took responsibility for AWRE Orfordness in Spring 1957. Unlike most of my previous moves, this one did not necessitate a domestic move as I was able to continue to live in Felixstowe and in the same house. One special feature which appealed to me was travelling to and from the AWRE site each day which involved boat trips over two rivers, the Deben and the Alde, in all weathers. I was issued with a Vauxhall Velox staff car in which I could make the 30 mile journey around by road if the occasion demanded but, mostly, I only used the car to make the frequent visits to Aldermaston which were required of me.

The Orfordness site was shared with a Ministry of Defence (MOD) establishment employed mainly to control the bombing range and the various ballistics tests carried out by the Ministry with both their own and RAF aircraft. Both sites were well away from the quay but the AWRE was even further towards the sea across a very large tidal ditch which provided an even more secure environment and was arranged so that even MoD staff were discouraged from visiting.

The AWRE staff had started as a small team in makeshift accommodation operating special telemetry, of which more later. A few months prior to my arrival a very large expansion was started and, typical of AWRE, was carried out with tremendous application and speed. On arrival I inherited a just completed modern single storey laboratory building for the electronics team

30. AWRE Explosives Pagoda

and three large ungainly looking buildings, nicknamed 'pagodas', for the explosives team(Fig 30). The latter were built for the special purpose of testing weapons like Yellow Sun and Blue Streak, complete with the nuclear bomb, but without the live nuclear core. In place of the core was a 'lookalike' dummy, having all the same physical characteristics of size, density, etc. These buildings on the explosives site were high with very thick hollow walls filled with shingle and with shingle piled up the sides. On top were very light roofs which were designed to present minimum resistance to an explosion in the main chamber of the building. The theory was that if we had a blowout everything would be funnelled directly upwards through the roof and would come straight down again thus ensuring that no debris fell on the village of Orford about half a mile away across the river Alde. Mind you, all the AWRE staff would be directly on the receiving end as the debris fell back to earth – a great incentive for the staff to avoid an accident! One of these buildings had massive installations of engineering equipment which could shake and vibrate the whole weapon through the total spectrum of frequencies which were likely to be encountered in aeroplanes, tanks and vehicles of all kinds. Another had temperature inducing equipment which could take a whole weapon through the complete specification range from very cold to very hot. The third was a very large centrifuge which again could take the whole weapon through the full range of G forces. I, not being used to explosives, felt very strange in this area of the site and never really relaxed in it. Thank goodness I had some excellent explosives experts on my staff who were thoroughly experienced in this work. However, being responsible ultimately, I was educated in the main safely regulations and had to visit the site frequently for checks. Apart from the overall administration my main interest was in the electronics work. When I arrived this was mainly concerned with very sophisticated telemetry and had been the job of the first AWRE team on the island. They were a very competent team but unfortunately the leader, a Senior Engineer, seemed to resent my appointment and very soon this had to be recognized and the 'powers that be' at Aldermaston had him returned to the main AWRE establishment. Since most of that team were recent recruits of my vintage we soon settled down to a good relationship and performance.

The telemetry was probably some of the most advanced anywhere. Its purpose was to monitor the behaviour of the detonating system as the bomb or missile was dropped or fired on the range. In order to achieve the all important critical mass to bring about a nuclear explosion the core was surrounded by explosive material, the tamper, in the form of a number of small sections all of which had to fire almost simultaneously. That meant, in practice, within very small parts of a second. If the explosion was not symmetrical there would be a 'blow-out' and critical mass would not be achieved. The telemetry team had to

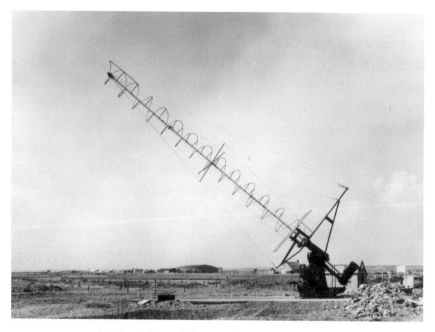

31. Special Aerial for Sputnik Satellite Detection

make innovative changes and developments to accommodate the different weapons and aircraft involved and were kept very busy.

My ultimate boss at Aldermaston was Dr Ewan Maddock, later Sir Ewan, Head of Trials as mentioned in the last chapter. He was a smallish man but an absolute bundle of energy and full of ideas. On one occasion he came into my office and informed me that the Russians were shortly to launch their first communications satellite, which was known as the 'Sputnik'. Pointing out what a nice quiet site we had from an electrical and electronic interference view point and which was miles from industry, he suggested we prepare a system to receive and examine the signals it would be transmitting at around the VHF band (100 MHz). One or two of the more recent members of my team were experienced in propagation and in aerial design and, as indicated in earlier chapters, it was an area in which I, myself, was familiar. Having given it some thought we procured an old Bofers Gun from a

Ministry Maintenance Unit in the midlands, The workshop whittled down a pine tree from the local National Trust forest and inserted it into the barrel. It was supported along its 40 foot length by nylon ropes and spreaders of insulation material to avoid distortion of the beam. A helix aerial of dimensions to resonate at the required frequency was wound around this and again supported by appropriate insulation material. The fact that several of us were yachting enthusiasts was fairly evident in the resulting aerial (Fig 31). The reader will readily appreciate how convenient it was to sit on the 'gun' and steer this aerial around in azimuth and in elevation and follow the Sputnik as it passed slowly across the sky. It became known as the 'Sputnik Chaser'. For the more technical, this aerial had a gain at 100 MHz of 22db and produced outstanding records of the signals coming from the Russian satellite. This work, I believe, is typical of the enthusiasm and innovation one can achieve with small teams in a small unit away from the main large establishment. Pride and enthusiasm were the basis of this achievement. The results were received with enthusiasm by the communicators throughout the several government departments concerned.

Ewan Maddock came down and congratulated us but, without taking another breath, he had another task for me. This was typical of the man who was one of the most 'press on' types I ever had the pleasure to work for and with. We continued to supply information to the communicators on Sputnik but Ewan's interest had switched. He informed us that the French were expecting to let off a nuclear bomb at their establishment in the Sahara at Regaine. Once again we were reminded that we had an ideally quiet site and we were to attempt to detect its effect in the ionosphere. This would provide important information about the behaviour of the ionosphere and therefore, at that time, on some of the vital communications in the high frequency (HF) sectors of the radio spectrum. These ionospheric layers have properties, which, depending on conditions which vary with the state of the Sun's activity, can act as a reflector of HF transmissions and send the energy back to earth at a distance from the origin known as the 'Skip Distance'. Energy is lost at each reflection but given sufficient power in the original transmission the signal can skip up and down a number of times and deliver information at a long distance. The HF spectrum supporting this process forms a very useful and important means of long distance communication with both civil and military applications. Any disturbance or interference with these ionospheric layers could therefore disrupt these important means of communicating over long distances before alternative means of communication by satellites became practical. Hence the interest in the effect of the French explosions.

Once again, my small team started to plan how best to tackle this task. Because the particular part of the HF spectrum for best results is so variable we decided to set up a transmitter and receiver system to cover the whole range 1Mhz to 30 Mhz. This started by obtaining from an RAF Maintenance Unit three redundant 'G' equipments which we modified so that each covered about one third of the required frequency range, about 10MHz each – with an acceptable performance over that band. The next problem was aerials to cover the same band. Once again, dictated by the need for reasonable efficiency we decided on three large Rhombic aerials, again each covering about 10 MHz. These aerials can produce a beam of coverage and were sited to 'look' to the south in approximately the right direction of North Africa. Each was constructed with poles, again from the local National Trust forest, set out in the required diamond shape with wires draped around them about fifteen feet above the ground. Each was of the order of 80 feet long.

Together, this transmitter / receiver and aerial equipment gave us the ability to adjust to the conditions prevailing in the ionosphere at any particular time. In fact we had a reasonably efficient adaptable HF facility between 1 and 30 MHz. Then came an important suggestion. One of my team, who was very knowledgeable on propagation, had an excellent idea prompted by the degree of flexibility we had in our wide band facility. He suggested we attempt to set up, for any particular state of the ionosphere, the frequency which neither passed through the layers nor skipped back to earth but was the critical frequency which would duct along the layer, thus avoiding the reflection losses. This required a degree of experience in interpreting the ionospheric prediction charts for any given period together with the very flexible wide band coverage.

Early in 1960 we were alerted to the French programme and, using the latest information on the state of the layers, a small team kept watch from about 03.00 hrs on 13 February. The reader will understand the tension in the team when it got to nearly 06.30 that morning and nothing had been seen. Then, suddenly, at about 0635, a pulse signal was received growing out of noise and from 07.30 onwards the whole ionosphere was suffering severe and widespread activity comparable with occasions when large auroras and sun flares occur and do disrupt communications. Of course we checked later that there was no such aurora activity at this time. We continued to record this very large disturbance for some time until the ionosphere returned to its normal state. Ewan Maddock was suitably impressed and these results were passed to the communicators who were equally pleased to have this information as part of their task of understanding and predicting the behaviour of vital defence communications (Fig 32).

During the five years I spent as Superintendent of AWRE Orfordness it will be appropriate to say a little more about the environment and our relationship with the locals over the river. Firstly, within my responsibility I had a fleet of three ex government landing barges with a crew of six recruited from the local fishermen – all real characters as one might expect. All the staff, vehicles,

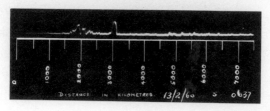

Looking South in the direction of Reggane.

This is a single shot picture taken from a number of records showing the pulse at 2,950 Kms. This pulse first appeared at 06.30 hours and continued for 10 minutes, fading at 06.40 hours, during which time it had a fading rate of 6 to 7 seconds and small amplitude change.

The more irregular wave form centered at 2,000 Kms is the first "hop" return

32. Nuclear Burst Effects in Ionosphere above Regaine

supplies, contractors and weapons etc. reached our island via these barges and Aldermaston allowed the building of a good modern slipway on both sides of the river to facilitate this vital support operation. Of course, we supplied the services as necessary to the MoD team also. AWRE also provided an excellent large car park on the mainland in Orford, which we shared with the public. Thus, we had the goodwill of the majority of Orford residents. We boosted trade in the two pubs, the Jolly Sailor and the King's Head, in the Castle Hotel, and in the two or three local shops. The Jolly Sailor was my favourite for lunch quite frequently although we also had an excellent canteen on site. I shall always remember the intense games of dominoes in the four ale bar which several local fishermen played regularly.

Some of the negotiations with the locals were quite amusing at times. I remember that on one occasion we needed to erect a reception building for security reasons on the mainland and chose a site at the back of the Quay at Orford. However, it was necessary to get permission to remove one large hut belonging to a local fisherman. This he had occupied on the site for many years. It was typically semi-derelict with several 'make do and mend' features. Nevertheless the owner put up a defence which would have been worthy of a QC. It was very convenient in its present site, it would probably not stand the move, its worth to the owner's fishing and overall financial situation was priceless, etc, etc. Finally he got a brand new hut of larger dimensions on a site which we provided still quite close to the quay, plus some compensation. Businesslike behaviour is not confined to the City of London!

Another event worth telling is when I decided to take one of the bargemen to the London Boat Show at Earl's Court. Fred Chambers was a very experienced sailor and earlier in his life had crewed on Sopwith's 30 metre yacht in International racing. Working for us at AWRE he was more or less in his retirement. Nevertheless Fred had not been far from Orford for a very long time. This visit to London was really rewarding for me since Fred was so obviously overwhelmed with everything he saw. One memory will always remain with me. In the early 60s some use of plastic materials was creeping into many products. Fred and I found ourselves in a crowd in front of a stand on which a very overdressed young salesman was eulogizing over one of the first 8ft plastic rowing dinghies. When he had finished his speel I turned to Fred saying "what do you make of that, Fred?" The reply, delivered in a stentorian Suffolk voice, was "well, that might be oright in the barrth room but that woddent be any bloody good on the River Alde". The crowd started to laugh, the salesman went puce and we beat a discreet but hasty retreat. Another incident centred around the Fairy Marine Stand. Moulded plywood boats were very popular and Fairys had their full range on show from a 10ft dinghy to their large Fisherman. As usual, each was attended by a glamorous blonde, brunette, redhead or dark-haired lovely. As we approached, Fred was muttering to himself "what do them mauthers know about boats?" However, we had intended to look carefully at a 12ft Firefly which was a favourite on the Deben and might also suit the Alde at Orford. This boat was being attended by a very nice blonde girl and a reluctant Fred gradually began putting questions to her. As an active member of a well known south coast sailing club she slowly gained his full attention. So much so that after about twenty minutes I had a hard job to get him away. As we walked off Fred turned to me in his typical Suffolk "well thars a bloody rumun. My wife has lived by the water all her life and still don't know the stem of a boat from the starn and thars that young gel knowing more about that than I do – thars a proper rumun!"

Another amusing incident whilst I was at Orford concerned an official visit by a party of the US Army headed by a three star general. After a useful technical exchange over several days we decided that on the Friday afternoon before they departed we would take them on a visit to the Norman Castle in Orford Village. This was, of course, a highly popular item on the week's programme and keenly awaited. The local curator gave an interesting presentation as we went around and up on the top as we walked the battlements he casually pointed out the 'pee' hole cut in the stone wall for the guard to use if 'cut short', so to speak. This was too much for the General who seized the opportunity to use it himself, whilst at the same time instructing his adjutant to take a descreet photograph. One can imagine the first party he and his wife would give back in America. "Me using the facility used by the Normans in their castle in 1066!"

At the time of my stewardship of AWRE Orfordness it must be appreciated that security in relation to anything to do with atomic weapons was about as high as it was possible to be. Sometimes it reached ridiculous proportions and I have seen letters and internal memoranda labelled 'Top Secret' even though they contained nothing more important than, say, cancelling a meeting or advising that a member of staff would be on a day's leave. In fact it was often said, I hope jokingly, that promotion at AWRE depended on how many top secret documents one held in the safe!

It will be no surprise, therefore, that security at AWRE Orfordness was at the very top level. In addition to all the boundary wires and observation posts, special precautions were taken to ensure that the several miles of steep shingle beach were secured by frequent patrols and well-placed 'lookouts'. During my time there were only two 'invasions'. On one occasion a fishing trawler with engine failure was blown ashore. This was easily dealt with in co-operation with the coastguard service although it took several days to get it removed.

This leads me to the one real security incident during my period at Orfordness which caused a full scale alert and operation involving not only my team but also the main security staff at Aldermaston. This second incident had all the makings of a comic opera. In the late afternoon a 12ft open dinghy with an outboard engine arrived in the middle of our stretch of beach which, even for a much bigger boat, was so steep as to be quite dangerous. The dinghy crew was an adult male and female and two small children. They were spotted as they approached the shore and were 'greeted' by three AWRE police officers each with a large dog – two German Shepherds and one large black Labrador – the latter snarling ferociously as was his approach to anyone other than his handler. All four looked scared and tired but their story was so unbelievable that AWRE security went into top gear. Firstly they claimed to have set out from Walton on the Naze, about ten miles down the coast, in nice calm weather. Around midday the SW wind blew up, as is not unusual on this coast, and when they tried to turn back meeting the waves head on threatened to capsize the boat so they got blown up the coast. The outboard was swamped and they were blown onto our beach. Of course, no one in their right mind would attempt such a trip even in a much larger boat. To make matters of more concern the man and woman were not married and had different surnames and the woman's name had a mid-european or even Russian ring to it. Aldermaston security went into red alert and all four were held and questioned for twelve hours or more before it was accepted that they were very silly holidaymakers who had unknowingly put their own lives in great danger.

There was a sequel to this story some years later when the National Trust took over Orfordness and the BBC 2 John Dunn Show made a programme in which I took part and told this story. A few days later the woman who had been involved in this incident rang the BBC and, having heard the programme, said she enjoyed it but that I had not stressed anything like strongly enough how terrifying the whole incident was from their point of view.

The Mission to Australia

Towards the end of my five years as Superintendent of AWRE Orfordness I was fortunate to have the opportunity to visit Australia. A weapon was in late stages of development for the Ministry of Defence, which was planned to be capable of carrying a nuclear war head. This weapon went under the rather attractive name of Blue Streak, which was designed for long range performance. It was to be fired from Woomera with a target area in the outback in the North West desert area of the Northern Territory. As part of the preparation AWRE was to make arrangements to use the special telemetry, which we had developed at Orfordness. The first part of the preparations was to visit the target area and choose the sites for five or six stations which would be needed to cover the area. I was fortunate to be asked by Ewan Maddock to undertake this assignment and I was to be accompanied by a Mr Stevens, an officer from the Ministry of Technology. The plan was for us both to travel out to Australia in a Britannia aircraft of RAF Transport Command and to link up with a team from the Australian Weapons Research Establishment (WRE) in Adelaide.

The flight out in the Britannia was quite gruelling. It was a non-stop flight except for refuelling stops and took about 41 hours. When we finally landed at Sydney airport it felt quite strange to be on solid ground. We had a stopover in Sydney to recover and stayed in the Astor Hotel overlooking Bondi Beach, which was as attractive as I had always imagined. The next morning I was up early and walked down to the beach for a swim at about 06.30. Fortunately several lifeguards were already on duty and somewhat amazed at this lone Englishman so early. One became quite friendly and decided to accompany me into the water. Having got somewhat used to swimming in the surf my guardian decided to get two boards and I spent the next hour learning and enjoying the first elements of surf boarding in quite big rollers; quite a thrill. Later that day we flew by Ansett Airlines to Adelaide and on the following day reported in at WRE Survey Department to their Chief Survey Officer, Trevor Nossiter, and a team of three Australians with whom we were to spend the best part of the next three weeks in the Outback. We were soon to realize that Trevor knew the Northern Territory as well as the back of his hand, so to speak. We all spent the next two days poring over maps and charts, taking account of the contours and various other features. We decided the areas we would start to inspect in detail for each of the six sites. All were planned to be within about 30 miles of the centre of the target area.

In the off duty hours over the weekend I had several delightful swims from the beach in Adelaide and on one occasion joined the many bathers rushing out of the water following a shark warning siren. I wasn't the last out either! Also I was entertained by an old Bawdsey colleague Roger Dippy and his wife. He was of 'G' Radar Navigation fame and now on the staff of WRE. The Dippys also took me out to the Barossa Valley, famous for its vineyards, and we visited several and tasted the produce.

The next morning we joined the Royal Australian Airforce DC3 which was to take us, by a roundabout route dictated by winds, to our intended destination which was a cattle station called Anna Plains in the Northern Territory about 100 miles inland from Broome and Port Headland. Our first call, however, was Woomera where we witnessed a Black Knight missile firing. We then flew west to Kalgoorlie where we spent the rest of the day and night. I don't remember the name of the hotel but I think it was 'The Grand'. I do remember it still had rails for tethering horses all along the front. I wonder what it is like now. It had the most delicious steak on the menu for dinner. The steak and fried eggs for breakfast next morning was almost daunting. Aboard the DC3 again we headed north towards Broome but distances were vast. On the way, we, for my benefit, flew at very low height over one of Australia's dead towns, Wiluna. It once was a large thriving town in the days of the great gold rush but had been completely deserted when the seam ran out. The effect of houses, pubs, one or two churches, etc., well preserved in this climate, was ghostly and weird with not one human being in sight.

We arrived over Anna Plains cattle station in late afternoon and as we were approaching the last hundred miles or so a high very black cloud seemed to be chasing us to get there first. The DC3's crew were very concerned because from experience they knew Anna Plains had only a dirt landing strip and if that rain cloud dropped its load before they could get airborne again they would be stuck, literally, for quite some time. However, they dropped us off with all our stores and luggage and as we saw them disappear in the distance the heavens almost fell in!

We were welcomed into the substantially built wooden station house by the manager and his wife who had emigrated from Kensington and seemed to be very content with their lives in the outback. We were told that Anna Plains was a cattle station of about a million acres and some ten thousand head of cattle. Water was not really a problem. At the time they had six bore holes in various parts of the station. They told us that feed for the cattle was the real problem and recently, since they had had very little rain in the last several years, they were losing a lot of cattle. The poor beasts on their last legs from starvation would get to one of the water holes and drink themselves almost literally to death. The first very sad job each morning was to drag the dead carcasses away. One can imagine how pleased they were to see the rain which would have an almost immediate effect on the sparse clumps of spinifex grass. We all had a meal together that first evening and then we returned to the WRE compound which was maintained permanently to provide a headquarters for the various expeditions made in the area. It had a large wooden hut for general use and large tents for sleeping. The area occupied by the station was in direct contrast with the surroundings. Outside the boundary the reddish brown earth stretched away into the distance with clumps of grass normally spread many feet apart. Here and there were pillars of rock. In contrast, the area around the station site was lush and a blaze of colour from hibiscus, jacaranda and other colourful plants. In addition to the main house there were houses for the staff and a number of buildings for various purposes connected with animal husbandry. The staff consisted of a number of white Australian and Aboriginal cattlemen and their families. The latter, we were told, decided that Stevens, who was a large man, had brought the rain with him and in their language called him 'Big white man bring rain'.

Part of the WRE site had a large car port providing shelter for three Land Rovers and we spent much of the morning loading them for the expedition into the desert. One was virtually a water tank, another had a load of survey instruments etc and the third had all the stores, sleeping bags, personal luggage and food. We made final plans and departed the next morning after a large breakfast at which we had the resident iguana lizard to visit us for his usual share of bacon. He and I became great friends on the

33. Telemetry Survey Party at Mt Phiar

several occasions when we returned overnight to the station. I called him Igor. At night the tent was full of flying insects such as locust, crickets, etc and this took a little getting used to before falling asleep.

Thus started, for me, a most memorable expedition. The area we had to cover had been surveyed for oil by the Western Australian Petroleum Company. They had taken a bulldozer and a compass and pioneered straight tracks north-south and east-west over the whole area, known as WAPIT tracks. These we used as much as possible to arrive at the nearest point to each of our chosen telemetry sites such as Mt Phiar (Fig 33). We all took turns to drive the vehicles and there was a degree of nervousness in Stevens and myself at the possibility of getting stuck in the soft red sand. Another feature of the area was the steep ridges, tens

34. Lunch in the Outback

of feet high, running for miles from east to west several miles apart. We all became very experienced in negotiating these hazards which were mainly 20 to 30 feet of sand hill with occasional clumps of rock. On the several occasions when it would have been wasteful to go back to Anna Plains for the night, we camped and slept out in the open in sleeping bags. The several occasions when we did camp out were unforgettable. Talk around the camp fire during a meal in the late evening after a hard day provided a unique experience. The clear cool atmosphere after the heat of the day gave a unique opportunity to appreciate the mass of stars dominated by the Southern Cross. Seen from the sleeping bag in the last waking moments after a very demanding day was one of those rare occasions when one has a glimpse of the vastness and depth of eternity in the otherwise everyday hurly burly world.

Another memory which registered deeply was the never failing manner in which Trevor was able to arrive at the one tree in tens of miles of desert to sit under for lunch, and how within minutes the tree would be the perch for dozens of the smallest multicoloured birds attracted by the chance of crumbs (Fig 34). On the last night out, after a hard day, we were chatting around the fire and several of us were bragging how none of us, even the Englishmen, had got a vehicle stuck. This boast must have registered strongly in Trevor's mind. Next morning we had tackled two or three of the ridges in the approved manner. That is, the lead vehicle would set out from the bottom getting up speed and roaring over the top. After a short interval the second vehicle would follow and then the third. All would gather at the normal level on the other side before proceeding again in convoy.

On this occasion, at the next ridge, Trevor went off first and disappeared over the top. I, with Stevens as passenger, was second to go. After the normal interval I set off. This ridge was not one of the bigger ones and I was taking it with ease until we reached the top and to my horror this was no ordinary ridge but dipped sharply down and up again – a double hump! Instinctively I put my foot hard down, we jumped much of the gap at the bottom, hit the upgoing slope quite hard and with all the luck in the world topped the second rise, and, in a state of disarray, arrived at the bottom to be greeted by Trevor with a grin like a Cheshire cat. Poor old Stevens nearly broke his neck on the canvas roof which fortunately already had a small slit in it. However, ten minutes went by and the third vehicle had not appeared so we trudged back up the slope to find it well and truly stuck in the dip between the humps. The extraction of that Land Rover deep in the sand at the bottom of the trough was very difficult. It was mid morning with sun beating down and the temperature in the nineties. We had two other Land Rovers with winches but even so we had to roam over a large area to collect sufficient brushwood to drive in under the tyres of the stuck vehicle. The whole exercise took the best part of two hours and we were all completely exhausted. This episode made one realize the difficulties even with a well-equipped team. It didn't take any imagination to understand the situation facing someone who had ventured into the Outback with inadequate planning and equipment.

We arrived safely back at Anna Plains in the late afternoon and spent the next day clearing up and making things shipshape. In the evening we made our farewells to all the friends we now had around the cattle station. The DC3 arrived at midday the next day as arranged and we watched the oasis of Anna Plains disappear in the otherwise featureless brown desert. In order to take advantage of the prevailing winds, we were to fly south east to virtually the centre of Australia, Alice Springs, where we would spend the night before flying on to Adelaide. For me this was a wonderful bonus. Alice Springs in those days, like Kalgoorlie, had the appearance of an American cattle town in the films, except the predominant vehicle was the largest motor cattle truck I had ever seen, and the town seemed to be the hub from which everybody was going everywhere. This town was also the centre of the famous Australian Flying Doctor Service and I was able to visit the museum which had wonderful artefacts including old aircraft and ground station radio communication sets. Alice Springs also had a lovely little church with one particularly outstanding feature. The window behind the altar faced the sun at midday and its centre piece, so to speak, was a huge cross, in what I believe was bottle glass, which was quite stunning with the sun shining directly through it.

The next day we flew to Adelaide where we spent a day or two reporting and clearing up. We then flew back to the UK on civil airlines via Sydney, Singapore, Bombay, Dubai and Geneva.

It is an interesting reflection that the day after landing back in the UK it was announced that the Blue Streak missile had been cancelled. I was pleased this had not happened earlier – look what I would have missed! It is amusing to note that some weeks later I received a cheque from the accounts department at Aldermaston for quite a large sum of money. Since I was not expecting any money outstanding from them, I phoned the department and was told it represented 'Hard Living Money' because I had had nearly three weeks in the desert. So I not only had the most exciting and enjoyable holiday ever but got paid extra to do it. Not bad, eh?

After this I settled down to the routine of AWRE at Orfordness again for a time but received warning instructions that we were all to be brought back to Aldermaston within months.

I left the AWRE in 1960 to take up an appointment with the Plessey Company in Ilford. I knew a Senior Director there, one George Smith, who tempted me into a position which would involve seeking new areas in electronics and civil aviation equipment which the company could exploit in new markets. It meant resigning from the civil service but the money offered was very tempting and, for the first time, I let this count. This turned out to be a disaster. Later, and soon after arrival, it transpired that I was expected to work for someone else I had not met before and we did not get on from the start. After two or three months, I applied to be released from my contract and after some considerable difficulties it was agreed that I could leave without any very onerous penalty..

Chapter 8

Automatic Landing for Real

It will not be a surprise that I did not start the process of leaving Plessey without having made sure I could arrange another job to go to. It was fortunate that BLEU, now at Thurleigh in Bedfordshire and still under John Charnley, had a vacancy in my old post there as Head of Guidance Systems. It meant 'eating humble pie' and also going back from my previous rank of Senior Principal Scientific Officer to a Principal. The fact that I was returning to the Government, I suspect, had a lot to do with my release from Plessey without penalty – they had future Government contracts in mind. This move back to BLEU turned out to be most fortunate. It gave me an excellent opportunity to get up to date on the progress made on the development of automatic landings during the four years since I was seconded to AWRE.

The work had moved on to consider the implementation of the blind landing system in the real civil aviation environment. The guidance team was now involved in overseeing the specifications and development and the acceptance testing of prototype equipment in the various industrial companies concerned. In addition, the UK was taking a leading role in alerting and influencing the civil aviation authorities of the world to realize the potential of automatic approach and landing as a major safety and regularity contribution to world aviation. In order to advance the acceptance of the UK proposals, it was necessary for both the proposals and the back-up statistics to be understood and supported by the world civil aviation community as a whole. The way in which this was organized and progressed required endorsements by the International Civil Aviation Organization (ICAO), which I mentioned earlier. This is an organization of representatives of some 150 nations, with headquarters in Montreal, Canada. In order to arrive at this formal acceptance, ICAO set up an All Weather Operations Panel (AWOP) with secretarial facilities. The Panel was made up of suitable experts from any ICAO member States that wished to volunteer. Thus it attracted an appropriate variety of interests including Government R and D scientists and engineers involved in Aviation and Airports, Airline Development staff including pilots and engineers. There were several associated interests such as the British Airline Pilots Association [BALPA] and the International Federation of Airline Pilots [IFALPA]. There were also members from air safety, from airport lighting and air traffic control. This panel not only considered the automatic landing system but also all the other facilities and services needed for real safe operations in all weather, including the airborne equipment, lighting, ground guidance beam equipment, obstacle clearance limits, regulations, etc.

Major national contributions were from the UK, USA, Australia, Germany, France and the Scandinavian countries. Russia and China were not members in the early days but have joined since.

I was about one year with BLEU when an Assistant Director post was advertised in the Directorate of Electronics, Research and Development (Aircraft Civil) DLRD (AC) in London. This was under an old friend from RAE and TRE, one Jim Briggs. I was appointed Assistant Director and was back again to a Senior Principal. The post, my first headquarters administrative job, was still closely associated with the automatic landing programme and, in addition, involved administering all developments in civil aircraft electronics and communications. The only snag was that I had to work in London and start regular commuting from Felixstowe, and this has continued almost unbroken until today as I am writing.

One of the first results of this appointment was that I was asked to head the UK team, which was set up to work with the ICAO AWOP which I mentioned earlier. For this work, the UK team was made up of experts in the four or five major contributing services which are important elements of the whole operation including, as I mentioned before, the aircraft and aerodynamics, the airborne guidance and control equipment, the approach and landing ground lighting systems, and the ground radio guidance beams in both horizontal and vertical planes, together with the distance to touchdown markers. In addition, there were a number of regulations and procedures to consider and to draft and finally to be formally agreed as standards.

The first AWOP meeting in 1962 was held in the ICAO headquarters in Montreal. The Panel had representatives with teams from the major contributing nations including France, Germany, Canada, Australia, Austria, Netherlands, Scandinavia and, of course, the USA. From time to time other nations attended and I apologise to those that my memory has left out. The secretariat was provided from ICAO and the secretary was an ex New Zealand Airlines pilot. Other organizations represented included the IFALPA and IATA. The Panel usually met for a three week session about three or four times a year and in the five years or so that I was involved we met in all the major countries who took turns in acting as hosts. This is common practice in all ICAO activities. At this first meeting I had the honour to be appointed Chairman of the Panel; a task that I held for the next four years. This unanimous decision was a great compliment to the UK and an acknowledgement of our leading position in the world in this development and of the excellent work of the BLEU over many years previously.

Towards the end of this meeting our UK team ran an excellent party in the old Laurentian Hotel where most of us were staying, and it became traditional to throw a party during the three-week sessions or to organize a local interest trip during one of the week ends.

Much hard work was done in this first meeting to set up the programme for the future and a number of sub groups were agreed to deal with major areas such as guidance, control, lighting, obstruction limits, meteorology etc. etc. All the work was aimed to determine standards and regulations which would ensure practical and safe operations of civil aircraft throughout the world. We also enjoyed several social events and some amusing incidents. On the first morning of the meeting the French representative arrived very late and looking extremely dishevelled. There had been a fire in his hotel and he had lost all his clothes. Oliver Carel was a very competent engineer and an exceptional cartoonist full of good humour. He became a great favourite with everybody. Alex Winnick, who represented the American Federal Aviation Administration (FAA), was also an outstanding character. He was a keen bird watcher and during a visit to Australia we all went on an expedition into the rainforest about one hundred miles inland from Melbourne where Alex was 'praying' to see a lyre bird. The forest was full of the most beautiful birds of all colours, parrots, parakeets, etc. Alex was creeping about very stealthily with huge binoculars when I, slightly ahead and walking normally, very nearly fell over a lyre bird. It was half concealed under a large bush and didn't bother to move – it was probably sitting on eggs. Anyway, Alex got his pictures.

This meeting in Melbourne was, I remember, very tough going and towards the end of the last day I was closing the meeting and was heard to say "all I need now is a beautiful sandy beach, a warm blue sea and sun". Captain Fox, the Qantas representative for the Australian pilots, came to me saying "do you really mean that – no night life – no women?" Having confirmed that was my only wish he convinced me I should break my return journey to the UK in Fiji. He also recommend me to stay in a newly built hotel 'The Fijian' on an island about forty miles south of the capital

Suva. The Fijian Hotel, as Captain Fox described it, shared an island with a native village and was accessed by a causeway across a river. It was, in those days, quite an incongruous situation with a very modern hotel as part of a native village. This sounded wonderful and I took little persuading to take Capt. Fox's advice. With his help Quantas made all the arrangements for the flight schedule changes and the hotel booking.

The next afternoon I departed Sydney and was delivered at 02.30 a.m. by Qantas Airlines at the airport for Suva, and stayed the remainder of that first night at the Mocambo Airport Hotel. For me this provides a vivid memory. Somewhere between paying the taxi and checking into my room I lost my wallet with tickets, currency, passport and all. Panic!! I immediately reported my loss to the manager and his reaction was swift. "Go and have a meal and if any of my boys have picked it up I will let it be known that I am aware of your loss and I'll be surprised if it is not returned." Since I had no money I was glad to have made good friends with the Qantas crew on the way from Sydney and they took me to the restaurant. When I went back to my room at 03.30 hrs, there lying on the doormat was my wallet – intact!

I would like to think that our hotel managers in London could have such faith in their staff.

In the late morning I travelled by taxi to the Fijian Hotel. The hotel, the village, and the whole area was idyllic and I spent three unforgettable days before continuing my journey back to the UK. On the first morning after breakfast I went for a walk along the beach. After covering about half a mile I was coming up to a sharp point of the shore when I began to hear a great shouting and laughing. As I rounded the point, there, in the lagoon inside the reef, were at least one hundred or more native men and women in a circle, which was gradually closing a large seine net gathering fish. As I, a lone Englishman, approached, an elderly man came running out of the water all smiles and in good English (it was their second language in Fiji) greeted me and explained that there was to be an important wedding that day and they were catching the fish for the feast. He invited me to join them in the water. I had no hesitation but waded in with him just as I was, in sports shirt, pants, shorts, socks and sport shoes. The climate was so friendly and the water at such a pleasant temperature that I didn't even hesitate. Soon I had my place at the net beside the Headman, as my mentor turned out to be. As the circle got smaller and enclosed a large number and variety of multi coloured fish, several gourd pots of liquid were poured into the centre of the circle. This, it was explained to me, acted as an irritant on the skin of the fish, which began to leap out of the water, whereupon all the men carrying spears proceeded to spear the fish which were then thrown into baskets carried by the women. The spearing was very accurate. Suddenly the Headman handed me his spear and invited me to 'have a go' so to speak. I found it very difficult. It was also very amusing how everybody stood well back but all convulsed in laughter at my efforts. Almost all Fijians seemed to be very friendly and very happy people. They are also very large people and even the women, who were generally rather beautiful in a comfortable way, seemed to have size twelve feet! This most delightful experience ended in an invitation to the dance in the village that evening which was to follow the wedding. I spent a very happy and interesting hour or two that evening, although dancing with these very large but very happy and unsophisticated women was somewhat daunting.

One observation is worth recording especially when related to comparatively recent events in Fiji. Earlier in the history of these islands (and there are some two hundred of them) we, the British, introduced labour from India and Pakistan to work the sugar plantations because the locals did not like to work hard and preferred to laze around and fish in the lagoon. For this reason the situation had developed such that these later generations of 'new' Fijians have, because of their more serious ambitions, begun to take over much of the profitable services such as taxis, sweet and tobacco kiosks, etc. When I asked my friend the Headman about this development and its possible political consequences for the future he gave one of his biggest smiles and said ' we are much bigger than they. We can take care of ourselves'. I must say that, at the time, I wondered and felt a little concerned for these big, friendly delightful people. As it happened, a few years back I was glad to see that they had decided to put their big feet down in the direction of governing their own country and I was somewhat disappointed that our politicians seemed not to have understood the situation and were expressing disapproval of the indigenous Fijians asserting themselves.

I left Fiji and its two hundred odd islands behind with a certain sadness, feeling I would probably not have an opportunity to return. On the way back to the UK we had an overnight stop in Singapore and I managed to cram in a short visit to Tiger Balm Gardens. I was also struck by the great differential between the rich merchants and the majority of poorer people. One saw grand houses almost side by side with poor native dwellings made up of corrugated iron sheets thrown together. It struck me that this almost obscene difference would stir up jealousy and envy to a point in the future when human relationships would break down into conflict.

Continuing the journey we called in at Karachi then at Dubai, Geneva and finally Heathrow. Back in UK, as ever, I felt more relaxed and, in spite of all the enjoyable experiences, glad to be back in England and particularly, later, in East Anglia.

Whilst in DLRD I made several other overseas visits as part of the AWOP activities and on each occasion there were certain events which stand out in the memory. It is worth recalling, particularly, the meetings in Australia and in Vienna. During the AWOP meeting in Melbourne I joined a number of the French delegation on a big game fishing expedition. We departed in a well equipped motor yacht around mid morning well stocked with lunch and of course, wine. Taking turns with two rods over the stern we all caught a number of Bonito which seemed to be in abundance and it was an interesting experience. However, some time after lunch I was sitting and chatting with a very jolly Air France pilot in their team when suddenly there was great excitement. The fin (sail) of a large sailfish was seen about one hundred yards astern and getting interested in the bait which was a highly coloured spinner. This beautiful creature about 10 feet long looked so elegant in its natural environment with a cloudless sky and a brilliant sun glistening on the small waves raked by only a light wind that I began to pray silently that it would not take the bait. After a tense ten to fifteen minutes the fish answered my prayers and disappeared back into the deep as silently as it had come. I was overjoyed but clearly I would not make a champion deep sea fisherman. My French companions were very disappointed.

In Austria I was able to include a visit to the famous riding school in Vienna to marvel at the control exercised over the horses. I was also very impressed that the Austrians were generally so well mannered and very helpful. One had only to stop on a street corner to study a map when the locals would rush up and offer help. I wonder if this is still the situation. Again, at the meeting in Copenhagen our hosts, the Danish Civil Aviation Department included a dinner in the famous Tivoli Gardens. During dinner our host challenged me to ride with him on the infamous 'up and over' gondola. Hanging upside down several times was certainly a breathtaking experience but it earned me quite a lot of brownie points.

During my time as AD/LAC2 there were two particular projects worth singling out from the great majority of somewhat mundane but demanding everyday administrative activities. I was selected to represent the UK on the team to plan the electronic navigation, radar and automatic landing requirements in the early planning of the Concorde aircraft. The UK team and our French opposite numbers met frequently in Toulouse and in London to plan the installations. The French team, I remember at one stage, was instructed by General de Gaulle that at the meetings in France his French team must work in the French language. In practice it turned out that when we, in the UK team, were trying to make useful contributions from our experience the French worked happily in English whereas when we were trying to understand their contributions they stuck rigidly to rapidly delivered French – 'one-up-manship'? At that time we had a number of companies in the lead on aircraft navigational aids of all kinds but under orders from our Government we passed on all of our experience and withheld nothing. It is interesting to note that now we have lost almost all our previous markets in those areas and France has had a thriving business through such companies as Thompson, TRT, Dassou and Thalis.

The other project during this period was one of tremendous interest technically but, as I will explain later, did not get beyond the concept and early specification stages. We in DLRD were located in the Adelphi building, off the Strand, in London at the time. One morning Ted Brunt, who was responsible for all communications in the British Overseas Airways Corporation (BOAC), came into my office and exclaimed 'Keith we are planning to put the £30 million Concorde over the Atlantic within a few years and we will never be sure that we will be able to make contact since HF is at times so unreliable'. This set me thinking. What was needed was a means of deploying three VHF stations to give cover across the Atlantic. I started looking at charts of the North Atlantic and considering the possibility of more weather ships. However, one day in the morning paper I saw a big article on oil rigs and platforms and that set me thinking. I made contact with Cammell Laird who were producing these rigs and they were very helpful and keen to be involved. Over several months I and one of my staff, Peter Hall, together with Cammell Laird developed a concept of a large platform looking rather like a huge hydrometer anchored to the ocean floor (Fig 35). It would be self-buoyant and have plenty of room for the modern aids such as VHF communication, radio direction finding and radar distance measuring (DME). It was also proposed to connect these Ocean Platforms to one of the transatlantic cables, thus making it possible for the Atlantic air traffic control teams on both sides of the Atlantic to provide information and instructions through the VHF communication service. There would be a deck on top to allow a helicopter to land for servicing and re-supply. In order to make the case more attractive from a financial point of view it could also have accommodation to attract use by oceanographers, deep sea fishing parties, weather study, fishery experts, etc. Raising the estimated finance of £12 to 14 million was expected to be difficult as always. Fortunately an old colleague, Bill Makinson, whom I had been involved with twice before at BLEU and earlier in Washington at the BAC was, at this time, Head of the National Research and Development Corporation (NRDC). This organization had been set up to encourage and support innovation and promising new proposals. He and his team expressed interest in this ocean platform project which, at one stage, seemed to be going along favourably. In 1965 I wrote a paper on the Ocean Platform project which was published in the Journal of the Institute of Navigation and I gave a presentation at the IATA conference of that year in Miami. However, as the idea began to be known more widely a major lobby began to build up of those who were planning satellite communications. They argued that they were expecting to deliver VHF services to aircraft on the North Atlantic routes within three to four years and the platforms would then represent a waste of money. This satellite lobby was very strong and they

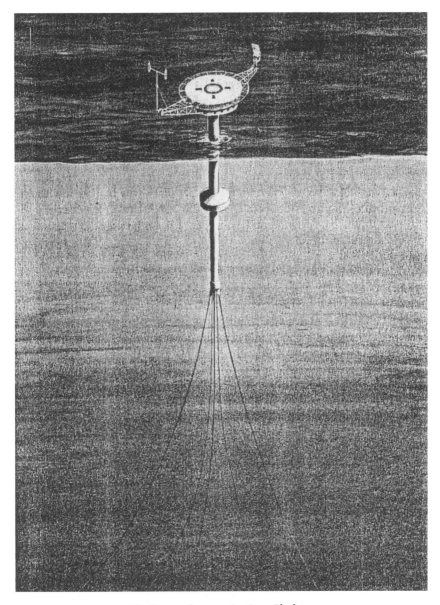

35. Ocean Communications Platform

succeeded in first delaying any decision on the platform and finally persuading those involved in financing the project not to go ahead. It is interesting to note that satellite communication services to civil aircraft over the North Atlantic were not available for many years after Concorde flights started, and are still, at this time, not fully authorized for use in civil aviation operations but used only for passenger communications to the ground.

During this period another very interesting development in automatic landing was initiated. An agreement was made between the aircraft company, de Havilland, the avionics equipment company, Smiths Aviation Ltd, and the Government which aimed to land the Trident civil airliner automatically at London Heathrow airport as part of a normal operation. The civil aviation department, then still part of the Ministry of Technology, were to provide the necessary ground aids including ILS beams, lighting etc. DLRD [AC] was one of the directorates involved in the Government programme and had an overall management function on the total project.

At this stage the tempo on the automatic landing programmes both in UK and in ICAO was speeding up markedly. Thus the Ministry of Technology decided to set up a new directorate, The Directorate of All Weather Operations (DAWO). This new directorate would coordinate all organizations involved in any of the component activities needed for civil aircraft to operate safely in all weathers. To my delight I was appointed as its first Director and promoted to Deputy Chief Scientific Officer. This post was to bring together all the departments of Government involved, the aircraft companies, the control and guidance equipment companies, the airport authorities, the Air Worthiness Authority, etc, etc. I chaired regular meetings and continued to head up our UK contribution to the AWOP in ICAO. In this post I reported to the Director of Air Safety and within the first few weeks I, as one who had spent most of his career in research and development areas, was brought to realize some of the workings of the top levels of the Civil Service. To appreciate this episode the reader needs to be reminded of the project with which I had been closely associated previously. This produced an agreement for the aircraft company, the makers of the automatic landing system and the Government to combine to make automatic landings in a Trident aircraft possible at London Heathrow Airport by a given target date. In the event the aircraft was ready but provision of the ILS landing beam systems by the Government (Ministry of Technology) was late. A parliamentary question no doubt 'engineered' by the industry, was placed by an MP and my Director of Safety placed this on my desk early one morning to draft a suitable answer for the Minister.

Of course, with my recent interest and enthusiasm for this project I, in my innocence, sent back a draft reply which, although I cannot remember it in detail, was along the lines that the Ministry were letting the side down and should get a move on with all urgency. Next morning an irate Director of Safety burst into my office saying 'This answer is useless – I can't ask the Minister to say anything like this! I will do it myself! The answer, when it appeared, was a classic of diplomacy which was unlikely to get any reaction but which could not be faulted in terms of truth or facts. It was what it did not say which was important. Another lesson learned, I suppose, but no wonder many of these situations are not properly understood and don't receive the treatment needed to resolve them.

However this appointment was inevitably an administrative job primarily and after about five years I began to get a little restive from lack of sufficient research and development content. At this point, I looked around the electronic industry to see if I could spot a company where new developments were likely to be supported. I began to get interested in the Decca Company which had shown considerable enterprise with its Navigating Systems, airborne doppler, ship control systems and airfield movement indicators. It was also involved in very accurate survey systems, ship control developments, etc. The Decca Chairman, Sir Edward Lewis, was a stockbroker by profession and the electronics company was really a hobby. It would be wrong to say he was not interested in profits but he was very keen to promote any proposal that had the possibility of enhancing the name of Decca. I got to know Harvey Schwartz, Bill White and George Hawker and when it became known I was getting restive, Bill White introduced me to Sir Edward and I was offered an appointment at a salary I could hardly refuse. I suspect that Decca's interest in me was based on my many contacts in several appropriate Government Departments, in the aircraft and airline Industries and in the atomic energy area. Decca was planning to enter the air traffic control equipment business and was already in negotiation with the Burroughs company in the USA who were well placed in this area with the American FAA.

I was a little reluctant to relinquish my role with ICAO as UK representative on the AWOP which was taken over by an old friend and colleague of BLEU days, Joe Morrall. He together with Geoff Harrison and Frank Gill set about getting the ILS, in particular, and all the other aids required for all weather operations sufficiently accurate and reliable to permit real all weather operations in Civil Aviation.

Thus, in Autumn 1972 I joined the Decca Navigator Company as Avionics Marketing Director, having negotiated an early retirement from the Civil Service at the age of fifty seven after thirty six years almost unbroken service. The only exception was the three months debacle with the Plessey Company which I mentioned earlier.

Chapter 9

Industry for Real

I joined the Decca Navigator company in the late summer of 1972 at the age of fifty seven. As I have already indicated the Decca Company was unique in several ways. The Chairman, Sir Edward Lewis, was one of the older and one of the last generation of bosses in the radio and electronic industry to have outstanding – almost dictatorial and eccentric – characteristics. Decca was based at Decca House on the Albert Embankment in London which was the seat of his 'empire'. One intriguing feature of Decca House which emphasizes my earlier remarks was that it had two lifts. However, one was exclusively reserved for the Chairman and no-one was allowed to use it unless invited by him or involved in meeting high level visitors. In the present day world it is popular to criticize such management behaviour but I have reservations when one contemplates all the present lack of respect and indiscipline that seems to have evolved from recent management methods.

Sir Edward had no formally appointed deputy and no succession plans and all his senior directors reported directly to him. Some, of course, seemed to have more influence than others. My immediate superior was a very experienced marketing operator, Bill White, who always seemed well placed with the Chairman. On the technical side Harvey Schwartz, Bill O'Brian and George Hawker were innovators and forward looking and for all of them I also had considerable respect.

At this time there had been considerable difficulties with the UK Air Traffic Control System which used the IBM 9000 computer systems, and a new replacent was being discussed. Just before I arrived at Decca, interest had been growing in possible contracts for air traffic control equipment which could involve a wide range of requirements for computers, displays, communications, radar, etc. A negotiation had already been initiated with the American firm Burroughs who had experience and credibility in supplying to the American Federal Aviation Administration. I, with my previous experience with the UK Civil Aviation Authorities and my links with the FAA through the AWOP, was quickly linked into this exploratory exercise, with consequential visits to the USA and much liaison with my erstwhile colleagues, now in the new CAA. As part of this planning we investigated possible links with other companies which would strengthen the ability to impress with any bid we might make. Firstly, to have a stronger position in the all important area of software development I helped to set up a new company – Decca Software Sciences Ltd – with a company I had had dealings with before called Software Services Ltd. I was made a director and chairman of its executive committee. In a similar exercise we formed another new company, Decca Smiths Navigation Ltd, with Smiths Aviation Ltd who were very experienced in computer control and overall systems engineering. In an attempt to interest my erstwhile colleagues in the National Air Traffic Control Services, (NATCS) we organized presentations, but in the long run the more longstanding companies in the business such as Marconi and Plessey continued to hold their place and it was almost impossible to break in.

Decca also forged wider links with Fujitsu in Japan who were already acting as the Decca Naviator and Dopper equipment agents in that country. This led to a liaison visit to Japan with visits to Tokyo and Kyoto. I spent a great deal of time with the company's agents in Tokyo and was very impressed with their dedication. I found the Japanese very polite and very friendly. I stayed in the New Tokio Hotel which had been built only recently. On arrival, around the middle of the afternoon I checked into the hotel, sorted out my various bits and pieces and then went down to the lounge for a cup of tea. I was somewhat surprised to have a very pretty girl waitress come up to the coffee table in front of me, kneel down, and ask what she could get for me. Although I am well aware that this is not in line with the normal modern ways, after a long journey by air, it was a very pleasant experience. Not long after I was back in the UK I read that the hotel had been burnt down and the fire had been started by a guest smoking in a bedroom.

During the latter period with the Decca Company I finally hit upon a very interesting project. Several years earlier Decca had pioneered a ground radar system designed to survey an airport and display all the aircraft and vehicle movements on the perimeter and on the taxi tracks as well as, of course, the runways. This facility was found to be invaluable to the air traffic controllers at London Heathrow Airport where it was installed. However, in those early days after the war it was considered that the only way to get the high definition required was to work on a very high frequency around 30 GHz. The performance was very good but the equipment required considerable maintenance effort and the expensive transmitter valves had a comparatively short life. Experience in the air traffic control equipment area led me to believe that a lower and more practical frequency could be used and the required definition and discrimination could be obtained using up to date display technology such as memory, refresh and interlacing techniques. In deciding how much lower the operating radar transmission could be, I suggested we should try the three centimetre wavelength on which the established Decca marine radar was operating. If this proved to be adequate then the new airport surveillance radar could be built around a modified version of the marine radar which was in quantity production. This, of course, should result in important cost savings and in a very competitive equipment.

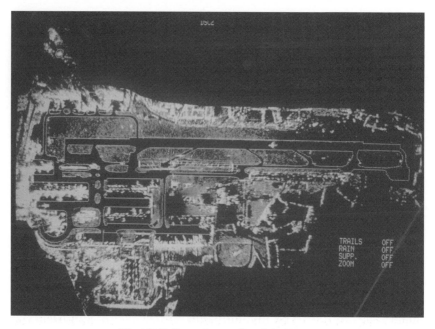

36. ASMI Operating at Gatwick Airport

My proposal was supported by the 'powers that be' and it was decided that I would have the assistance of a Decca development team located near Edinburgh airport at Linlithgow. This was an excellent choice and this team had all the skills needed to tackle such a development, which, as a result, moved ahead skilfully and quickly. In the meantime, with the support of some of my erstwhile colleagues in the CAA, I was able to talk the authorities at Edinburgh airport into allowing us to install the first prototype on that airfield on an ideal site for obtaining an overall view around the airport. We decided to name the new development 'The Airfield Surface Movement Indicator'; ASMI for short. As can be seen from Fig 36 showing the ASM Display, the resulting image was excellent and, as anticipated, the marketing price was very competitive. The ultimate accolade was, perhaps, that we sold an installation to Amsterdam Schipol airport in competition with the Dutch Philips company.

Whilst I was still with Decca I received in the New Years Honours of 1980 the award to the Most Excellent Order of the British Empire (OBE). This honour was for my work in the Civil Service and in particular for my contribution to All Weather Operations for Civil Aviation.

Whilst Sir Edward was fit and well, Decca was a very exciting and pleasant company to work with. However, after about eight years with the company its fortunes suddenly changed. One year we were in profit to the tune of £15 million and the next we were in the red by several millions and an attractive target for a takeover. During this period Sir Edward became ill with leukaemia and it was now that the lack of the succession plan, that I mentioned earlier, made the company even more vulnerable. Bids were made by the Marconi Company and by Racal, and in the end Racal, supported by the wishes of senior Decca staff, won the day.

Racal was a very different company in that it was very businesslike and was no longer prepared to support projects which could enhance the name of Decca unless, at the same time, they were suitably profitable. As part of the takeover process each senior person with a major project was interviewed by the CEO, in the presence of the new chairman. I was called in on my ASMI project and after a few pleasantries we discussed this project and ASMI was clearly not a choice Racal type product since it needed too much investment for too little return. I had previously applied for finance to develop a Mark II version but the returns predicted were not sufficient. Clearly, up to that time Racal, who were used to turning out 50,000 army radio sets on a single contract, had little understanding of the capital goods industry. I left Racal within a year of this interview but I have been told since that the original version of ASMI sold quite well for various airports overseas.

It subsequently turned out to be very fortunate that during my period with Decca I was made the company's representative to the Trade Association EEA (Electronic Engineering Association) and, particularly, was a member of that organization's Aviation Division. A little later, as its Chairman, I represented the Division on the Civil Aviation R & D Board or 'CARDBOARD' as it was often called. The programmes involved a large variety of electronic technology and equipment as applied to aircraft and to their supporting ground systems. The Board was expected to anticipate requirements and produce annual reports, giving guidance to the authorities and to their operating departments to keep UK civil aviation in the forefront of services and facilities. The chairman was my old boss and colleague John Charnley.

Clearly, Racal was not my kind of company at that time, probably because it was efficient and successful and had a very limited interest in R&D compared to Decca. I finally decided it was not for me. My final decision to retire from Racal came over an incident, strangely enough, in America. I had a new boss and, although I admired him as a business man, he was not very informed in radar, radio and communications. I did not really hold that against him, my concern was based more on the rather arrogant and bombastic way in which he tried to press others into his views rather than ask for advice. Thus, on the visit to a company in the States whose navigation equipment we were considering to make under licence, we were in the MD's office and he was eulogizing about a special aerial design which was part of their new system. An assistant brought it in and the MD started to describe it. It was very substantially the design I had met many years previously on radar work at Bawdsey before the war and was described in the Amateur Radio Handbook on Antennas. Thus, I didn't need to make any detailed examination of it. My boss interpreted this as not having enough antenna knowledge to take part in an informed debate on this specimen. He turned to me and quite rudely blurted out "For heaven's sake, don't you want to examine it, man!" At that moment I was sure our relationship wouldn't work and made up my mind to leave. It is ironic that after the war I had received a Government award in recognition of my development work on advanced ground and airborne aerials.

On return to the UK, I discussed this situation with friends in the Trade Association (EEA), and it so happened they were expanding the secretariat and wanted someone to administer the Aviation Division on a two days a week basis. Meantime my Racal boss had decided that he didn't think much of me either and suddenly announced that I must retire – I was, of course, 67 years of age and well beyond the Racal retiring age – and he offered me two days a week consulting for a period to run down gradually. I don't think I ever had more pleasure in turning the offer down flat. Thus, I retired from Racal in 1982 and took up the EEA offer.

Chapter 10

A Bright Twilight with Some Serious Reflections

A Trade Association Consultant

The move in 1982 from RACAL to the Electronic Engineering Association, a leading Trade Association dealing with a wide range of electronic and avionic technical and policy issues, had been encouraged by my old friend Jock Speedie the Secretary of the EEA. It was planned as a two day a week consultancy to manage the Aviation Division. This group met every other month and dealt with all the electronic services and equipment associated with aviation, both civil and military. I was very familiar with the work of the group since, as a representative of Decca and later, of Racal, I had been its chairman on several occasions.

Again, I was fortunate in this move. It turned out that the EEA was on the verge of an expansion and needed more effort in the technical secretariat. I worked four days during the first week and this set the pattern for the next twenty years. However, much of the work within the Trade Association has been administrative and routine, acting as secretary to several committees in the communications and avionics areas. The main task has involved setting up meetings with suitable agenda, taking notes of the meeting and preparing and distributing the minutes. Although this has amounted to a very considerable amount of work and effort it is not a very interesting subject for readers of this book and they will understand, therefore, why these twenty years are contained within a page or two. Now, twenty years later, I am still doing four days each week as I write this. My arrival was timely since Jock himself needed to put more effort into the general administration of the Association. In addition to the Aviation Division I gradually took over committees dealing with other areas of communications and associated spectrum issues. In the UK I became a member of the United Kingdom Industry Space Committee (UKISC), which was jointly sponsored by the Society of British Aircraft Companies (SBAC) and the EEA.

I also continued as a member of the Civil Aviation Research and Development Board, which was administered by the Civil Aviation Authority and now, as I said earlier, was chaired by my old friend and colleague Sir John Charnley. Recently, having been a member of one of their committees for several years, I have been appointed to the Telecommunication and Navigation Advisory Board of the British National Space Centre (BNSC) which generally administers the UK Space programme and organizes the space interests of the other Government Departments.

These commitments also involved considerable travel in the major European States and, as part of these activities, I represented the EEA and the UK on a number of European Committees and on groups dealing with common European and, in some cases, global policies and standards.

Since the early days of the EEA in Leicester Square there have been several changes. In my twenty years with the Trade Association I have worked for five different Director Generals, have seen and survived four mergers, and moved from Leicester Square to Russell Square. At the time of writing we, the FEI, are in the middle of yet another merger, this time with the Computer Software and Services Association (CSSA). The combination will certainly result in the largest trade association in electronics in the UK. Big is not necessarily better – we shall see. We are now to be known as 'Intellect'. Heaven knows why!

During my twenty years with the Trade Association I have been closely concerned with such new development projects as GSM mobile phones, Private Mobile Radio (PMR), Smart Cards, 'e'-Processes for Local Government, the EU Galileo Navigation Satellite project, the Home Platform developments, etc.

I have been pleased, but understandably surprised, that I am still consulting on four days a week at the age of eighty seven. For one reason or another I suspect this is unlikely to continue much longer.

The Supporting Domestic Structure

It seems appropriate at this point in my story to mention a number of important personal factors which have helped me to maintain such a long, active and enjoyable career. Firstly comes good health and good fortune. After that I owe a very great deal to my wife Dorrie who has been a marvellous wife despite the very great difficulties concerned with her own health together with those associated with supporting our disabled daughter Judith which I discussed in some detail in Chapter 4. In spite of this Dorrie has provided a first class home which has always been maintained at the highest level of tidiness, cleanliness and comfort. Dorrie is an excellent cook and we have consistently enjoyed good nourishing food.

Dog Lovers

Dorrie and I both are dog lovers and I am sure that our comparative fitness up till now – well into our eighties – has a great deal to do with dog walking. All through our married life we have had dogs and walked miles and miles with them. We have had six and all have lived into double figures. They have all been great company for Judith.

Our first dog was a beautiful brown and white Pyrenean Mountain dog weighing eight and a half stone named Peter. After the war and whilst we were house hunting in Felixstowe, we stayed for a time with my in-laws. Peter lived next door with an RAF family and we got to know him well over the fence. When the owners were posted overseas we were asked if we would look after Peter for two years. This we could not do as we could never give him back when the time came. He went to some friends further away. Some months later we received a letter that Peter was being badly treated and we could have him 'for keeps' if we wished. I collected him from a filthy concrete stable in a terrible condition. He recovered quickly with us and enjoyed five years of loving care. Peter had a very friendly temperament and I only saw him angry once when a dustman, overwhelmed by his size, threw the empty metal dustbin at him as he fled out of our gate. Who could blame the dog.

A more amusing incident occurred when late in the evening after dark three well inebriated lads were being rather rowdy as they proceeded along the pavement on the other side of our five foot wooden fence, I invited Peter, playfully, to 'see them off'. His best guttural growl caused one of them to look over the fence just as Peter put his front paws on the fence and looked him full in the face at eye level. The man fell back shouting to his friends "a bloody polar bear!" His chums literally fell about with laughter.

The next dog was the black German Shepherd who became very attached to Dorrie. We collected him at four months and named him Timber. At eighteen months he made an attempt to assert himself as top dog and started a low growl if I got close to him as he was feeding. He also showed increasing signs of belligerence if I went close to Dorrie. I read a book by a German trainer of German Shepherds who predicted this development at eighteen months and recommended a thrashing with a light bamboo cane on an appropriate occasion when Timber's behaviour warranted it. There came such a good occasion when I tried to persuade him to leave the lounge one evening when friends arrived who were not happy with dogs. Timber rebelled and I took him out and struck him lightly until he stopped snarling. From then on we were the best of friends. Timber was the only dog I have had to hit to be obedient.

Timber was followed by a beautiful little Beagle we named Chopper. He became a great favourite with my daughter Judith who delighted in his impish behaviour. He also seemed to understand her disability better than our other dogs and they were close friends. Later on when Chopper was about six or seven, I was invited, quite out of the blue, to make a home for an Afghan hound. A prominent breeder became concerned about the home into which she had sold one of her dogs. The dog was being beaten by the husband to upset the wife, whose dog it was. The breeder promptly bought him back and offered him to us, through a mutual friend, for free. Rufus was a large and very handsome dog but very nervous and particularly of men, for obvious reasons. He quickly made friends with Dorrie and Judith. He and Chopper became great friends with the latter very much the leader in charge.

The day I collected him from Ashford in Kent I drove into our drive, shut the gates and let him out. He immediately rushed up the garden over a five foot wooden fence and disappeared into the marshes at the back of north east Felixstowe. My wife and I could not keep up with him and if he, with all his long flowing hair, had not got stuck fast in a V shaped ditch full of mud in the marsh we would never have caught him. Rufus settled down to be a most loveable animal and a great friend of all the family. He took a lot of grooming and looked very elegant for up to five or ten minutes afterwards. Soon after that he could be described as 'wot a mess'. Rufus died at about ten years leaving Chopper on his own for a time and he was much missed.

After Rufus and Chopper we gave a home to a fine Irish Setter.

He was a lovely animal with a very beautiful bronze red coat. When we first got him his name was Red. However, with elections in the offing, we felt we must rename him but with something similar. We decided upon Gregory, Greg for short. Greg was a large, handsome and very loving animal and he and I were particularly close. He was not as 'scatty' as most red setters but I'm afraid he was just a little 'dim'. However, he was a great favourite with everyone. Greg died at the good age of 12 years and then we gave a home to our present dog from a local rescue kennel. Twiggy is the first bitch and the first mongrel we have had. She is mostly Border Collie with some terrier and is certainly more intelligent than any of the other dogs except perhaps the Beagle, Chopper. She also needs more exercise and is certainly helping to keep Dorrie and me fit. Twiggy has an element in her character which we also noticed in Chopper. Both were intelligent yet could be exasperatingly disobedient at times when asked to carry out some request. They both understood exactly what was being asked of them but would not respond. Yet, often when one had turned to some other activity one could look round and the dog was conforming "I knew what you wanted but I will do it in my time!" As a family I believe we make more fuss of each dog as we have had them. I suppose, after six different animals, we have become more understanding. Some would say soft!

Gardening

One of my main activities which has made a major contribution to my healthy and above average contented life has been gardening, which I am still continuing at this time. As I mentioned in an early chapter, I became interested in gardening at an early age in Halesworth where both my grandfather and my uncle were excellent tutors, especially in producing vegetables. Each year since we moved into our present house in Felixstowe I have raised crops of all the common vegetables and we seldom have to buy vegetables – possibly the odd lettuce and some tomatoes out of season. Last year, for instance, I forgot to put in any onions! Except for one or two periods, I have done all the necessary digging and heavy work. There is nothing so satisfying as eating home grown vegetables, but now, in my eighties, I am seeking more help with digging and lawn mowing.

Sailing

Another great delight of mine has been sailing. From the mid thirties, when I joined Bawdsey Research Station and started learning to sail with the help of a good friend and colleague, Brian White, I have sailed regularly until two seasons ago in 2000. At this time I decided to stop as I realized that in my eighties I no longer had the agility or the sense of balance required to continue safely. Of course, I miss it but I've had a good 'innings' from any viewpoint.

My first boat was a rather heavy 12ft clinker built dinghy with a large gaff and lugsail. This I used off the beach at Felixstowe when we were living in a flat on the front overlooking the North Sea. I became quite skilled at launching into the surf, but it was a heavy slow boat. I also caught cod, skate and lobsters frequently. One interesting event is worth a few lines. One Sunday afternoon I had arranged to go lobstering with a friend and had gathered a pail full of bait (discarded bits from the local fish shop) which I put overnight in our allocated coal shed under the flats. Unfortunately the wind blew up on the Sunday and we had to abandon the trip. My wife rang me at work on the following Wednesday saying the proprietor of the building was complaining that something had died in our coal bunker. My friend and I immediately planned to go lobstering that evening. We were hardly able to stay in the boat with the stinking bait but we put our six hoop nets down three times during thirty minutes each side of high water and caught 22 lobsters. Normally I would have expected to catch one or two at most. No one will ever convince me that lobsters can't smell!

The next boat was a rather pretty little Bermuda rigged clinker built wooden dinghy which again I sailed off the beach. During this period I joined the local sailing club at Felixstowe Ferry and started crewing for a local industrialist, one Felix Atkins, in his 12ft Firefly which we raced every week in the season. Fee, as well as being one of the nicest men I've ever met, was known widely on the East Anglian coast as an excellent helmsman and an accomplished tactician. I learnt a tremendous amount from him and we won races at regattas and also in the Felixstowe Ferry Sailing Club's season points competition on several occasions. I shall remember for the rest of my life the thrill of planing in a strong beam wind in a 12ft racing dinghy with the bow wave at one's side and at shoulder height.

Since I gave up dinghy racing at about the age of fifty five I have sailed a very nice 15ft open day boat of Swedish design called a Vitting. It had a very high performance for this type of boat. It would plane easily with a fresh breeze and I have spent many happy days sailing single-handed on the Deben, Orwell and Alde rivers and between them. I was in the habit of beaching the boat at Ramsholt, Waldringfield, Orford or at Snape for lunch. The sun trap beach at Ramsholt, sheltered by cliffs and facing south, was a favourite.

I gave up sailing when, as I have said, my balance and agility began to fail me.

Concorde

One of the biggest thrills of my life was a flight on Concorde.

For my eightieth birthday Dorrie and Judith presented me with a ticket for a trip on Concorde and on 6 August 1995 I, together with several other intending passengers, gathered in the VIP lounge at Heathrow Airport as guests of British Airways. We were right royally entertained throughout the whole adventure.

Anticipation began to rise on boarding and during the roll out so that on reaching the runway it was already at a high level. This was nothing to the excitement of the take-off which, for me, was the greatest thrill of the whole operation. The flight over the Bay of Biscay and out over the Atlantic was smooth and comfortable but the supersonic flight was almost a disappointment since, if it had not been indicated on the instruments which were repeated in the passenger cabin, there was little sensation and at over forty thousand feet little to give any sensation of speed. The landing back at Heathrow was, for anyone used to flying, pretty normal.

What an incredible feat of advanced engineering this aircraft is and such reliability over twenty eight years for a project designed around the very frontiers of technology. A tremendous credit to both British and French designers and industries.

A Miscellany of Serious Random Thoughts from My Experience

Having spent thirty four years of my career in the Civil Service, over forty years in electronics and a total of over seventy years in research and development, I now intend to give a few thoughts and reflections on important issues which I believe should concern those responsible for the performance of the UK Government, the Civil Service and the Electronics Industry as I have experienced them all in action over this long period ... Clearly the readers will have their own views on these issues and many may find them controversial, but if they generate thoughtful and useful discussion they will have served my purpose.

The Loyalty Factor

At this point in my career I am, as I write, in a strong position to compare experiences between the Civil Service and Industry. I suppose the factor I noticed most during my time in the Civil Service was that there seemed to be a minimum of jealousy between the individuals and divisions whereas in industry at all levels, individuals seemed to be looking over their shoulders at everyone else and divisions were very jealous of their own patch, even, in some cases, to the point of being prepared to take actions in the interests of their own areas at the expense of the company as a whole.

Human Relations Factors

Again, in the Civil Service the human relations were always well considered whereas in Industry, in my experience, there used to be very little attention to such issues. However this situation has been improving steadily in recent years and is now in my opinion in danger of being somewhat overdone. For instance I was always expected to arrive at work on time and blaming other reasons for being late was accepted only on very rare occasions. Many employees now don't seem to accept that it is really their responsibility to make every effort irrespective of the circumstances. For instance, in my youth, if the train was late then one was not leaving enough margin and should be catching an earlier train.

Efficient Working

Another interesting reflection concerns the comparative efficiency of the several organizations in which I have worked, I have no doubt that the AWRE was, during the period I am able to judge, by far the most efficient. Because of the pressure of the political situation, money and accountants never seemed to be a factor. For this reason work programmes and objectives were invariably met on schedule. When I remember the way in which some projects in the traditional Civil Service were delayed, extended and constantly and grudgingly kept going on minimum injections of money I am quite sure there can be no question which produced the greatest cost/benefit result. To a large extent, under the pressure of competition and the market, most successful competitive Industry compares reasonably well with my memory of AWRE in this regard.

Main Establishment/Outstation Relationships

A further observation of interest, particularly related to the civil service experience, concerns the outstation relationship to the main establishments. The observations which follow come from the following relationships of which I had direct experience, namely the Airborne Radar team and its parent BRS and later the TRE Radar team detached to RAE, BLEU and its relationship to both TRE and RAE; and the AWRE Orfordness and AWRE headquarters at Aldermaston. In all the cases I was impressed at the dedication and achievements of the enthusiastic outstation teams. In almost all the cases there seemed to be a large jealousy factor from senior officers in the parent establishments at the innovation and progress achieved in the outstation teams – Ewan Maddock was one exception. In almost all cases there were continual efforts to bring these smaller teams back into the main establishments irrespective of their successes. In the longer run, I believe unfortunately, these efforts were invariably successful.

National R & D

In this last chapter I think it is also appropriate for me to make comments about the Electronics Industry which I have served in one way or another since 1936. My hope is that my views will be seen as an attempt to be helpful as a result of long experience. Almost my whole career has been in Research and Development

(R&D) and naturally the majority of my comments will relate to activities in that area.

Between when I first entered the R& D world and up to the present time there has been a very great change in both the Government and the Industry thinking and approach to this area which is so important to national performance and prestige. In the days immediately before the 1939 war and for a time immediately afterwards, the Government sponsored large research programmes in many disciplines and were supported by a number of Research Establishments. In my area of interest the Royal Aircraft Establishment, the Radio Research Station at Slough, the GPO Station at Dollis Hill and the Bawdsey Research Station were examples. The R&D programmes were heavily augmented by large cost/plus contracts in Industry. Today these establishments either no longer exist or their budgets and staffs have been severely reduced, as has the value of the supporting contracts available to Industry.

The Attitude of Mind of the Leaders of the Civil Service and of Industry

Again, in the days just after the war there were, in my opinion, many more strong minded senior men of vision in high places in the Government, in the Civil Service and in Industry than we have today. Projects such as the 'Automatic Landing of Aircraft', the Concord Supersonic Airliner, the TSR 2 aircraft and the GSM Mobile Telephone are good examples.

Almost everyone now seems to be suffering from 'short-termism'. Very few politicians, civil servants or those in the Board Rooms of Industry seem to be prepared to look further forward than two to three years. It seems that nothing which cannot produce immediate business and add to the bottom line in the accounts department within two or three years is of interest. Many will argue that the pressures of competition and staff reductions make this attitude essential in the present situation in order to stay in business. I seriously question this in many cases. It could well be that it is a 'chicken and egg' situation and had there been more long term planning and investment in high quality R&D staff and facilities in the past ten to fifteen years the situation would be very different. In this fast moving high technology world a continuous and healthy forward looking research programme is essential. The bigger projects, such as Automatic Landing, have had to be nationally led and funded. For example, from the beginning of the research programme to landing a Trident airliner with passengers at Heathrow Airport took about fifteen years. It is unlikely that any company or collection of companies could have undertaken or funded such a major project, involving hours and hours of expensive flight testing. Today the French government still supports and funds a number of large and exciting national projects. The Americans are well known to allow their industry to work quite large civil developments into their big national defence contracts where appropriate. Our government seems to want the private sector to take more and more of the funding and the risk. It seems that if a good proposition is put forward the automatic response is likely to be ' if you think it is such a good idea you get on with it and fund it'. Little wonder the UK is now steadily losing its long standing reputation for innovation and achievements in leading edge technology. Fortunately, through the Research Councils, our academics are still well placed in global credibility but I understand that sadly more of their work is exploited abroad than in the UK.

Risky leading edge research needs to be supported Nationally and cannot always be successful. Nevertheless if there are no risks taken there are seldom any outstanding achievements. It is also arguable that if ten R and D projects are undertaken and only one or two are successful they will more than justify the over all investment.

UK Government Spectrum Auctions

The Radio Spectrum is, and has always been, in great demand and in several bands can rightly be regarded as a scarce resource. Recently the Treasury has introduced a system of auctions to determine the allocation of certain bands relating particularly to future mobile telephone requirements. The process of requesting bids in sealed envelopes and allocating to the highest bidder is a reasonable way to deal with a scarce commodity and has been used in most countries. However, the recent process introduced by the UK Government encouraging interested companies to bid in open rivalry is, in my opinion, quite unacceptable. It has, in this case, resulted in some of our most successful mobile phone companies bidding against one another up to ridiculous figures to secure what – to them – is a vital stake in their future. Some have now borrowed billions of pounds to secure for the future this allocation of spectrum and are now saddled with a debt of several billions. Paying off the interest on the borrowed money is a tremendous overhead. Even if they survive there will be less money available in the immediate future for important new developments and they will be at a disadvantage to their foreign rivals, all of whom have found their Government's – may I say more intelligent – ways of making their spectrum allocations more helpful.

I cannot understand how our Treasury are prepared to risk ruining some of our most successful world leading high technology companies or at best presenting them with a serious handicap against their world competitors, all for the sake of putting a few billions into the Chancellor's pot.

Modern Communications

I feel obliged to make a few comments on modern communications. Of course there have been very great changes in the fifty years I have been involved in the communication business. My views are that modern communications are, like the curates egg, 'good in parts'. Let us consider the old work horse of communications, namely the telephone. To many people throughout the world it is still the primary facility in this service. However, on many occasions now a call will be answered by an answering service saying ' the person is not available or away from the desk – please leave a message'. Time and again the message is not responded to. Another more irritating response is that the caller is given a number of options followed by more and more options and often reverting to the original number and being presented with the same response again and so on ad infinitum. Meanwhile the caller is being charged to get nowhere – a telephone company benefit? Recently I have been pleased to hear that several of our leading firms in the City of London are insisting that all incoming calls must be answered by a human voice.

Again in a way, the modern e-mail would claim to offer services which more than make up for the reduced usefulness of the telephone. It is, of course, quite indisputable that to e-mail a simple question to Australia and receive a reply by return in minutes and at little cost is terrific. There are however, hidden snags. I know of several business colleagues who have admitted to having upwards of one hundred e-mails unconsidered for periods of days. I however, accept that e-mail is a great facility and particularly good for fast simple announcements and very simple 'yes/no' questions an answers. When they are used for long argumentative statements I find it very difficult to enter into an informed discussion and, even worse, an argument on e-mail, since it lacks the many other clues of body language and eye to eye exchanges which are so important in human communications, particularly when resolving disputes.

Government Targets

I have no doubt that target dates are very useful in any longer term project. However, they need some reasonable consideration before setting them in stone. I am by nature an optimist but I get very irritated when target dates are set as a result of political interests and on the advice of 'spin doctors'. Currently there are one or two good examples in my area of interest The target to have a large proportion of the general public using interactive digital facilities on the domestic TV set within the period up to 2010 is, I believe, optimism gone mad. We shall see.

This leads me on to the comment that the modern ICT technology to achieve these objectives has a long way to go in development towards equipment quality, continuity of service and reliability before the ordinary citizen will accept it. It needs to undergo a revolution if it is to reach the levels of ordinary domestic equipment and services that citizens have learned to expect. In fact, I believe that the high technology ICT industry will need to undergo a step change in quality requirements such as the Japanese achieved with their car industry some twenty or thirty years ago.

The Deterioration of Social Standards

During my lifetime I have seen great changes and many represent a lowering of standards of all kinds, and I do not believe we are the better because of this. Whether one looks at child discipline, parental behavioural control, adult behaviour towards one another, the tendency to 'dress down', the predominance of money and professionalism in sport etc ... I believe all of these and very many others are contributing to a sadly deteriorating environment for the human being and for this planet in general.

Commuting

From the time I left BLEU at Bedford in 1956 I have commuted regularly by Anglian Railways to London, which is over forty years. This has involved a car journey from Felixstowe to Ipswich of about 12 miles. The journey by rail is between 1 hour and 1 hr fifteen minutes at best to Liverpool Street and then by tube to, firstly Waterloo and a walk to Decca House on the Albert Embankment; later to Leicester Square and EEA and, currently, to Russell Square for the FEI. Leaving home about 06.00 hours and arriving at the office normally about 08.15. My record commute, however, was when Racal took over Decca and decided to move out of Decca House and into the Decca Building in New Malden. This meant an additional train journey from Waterloo to New Malden and then a bus ride to the plant arriving at about nine thirty. In all, this journey took some three and a half hours, seven hours a day travelling. Crazy? Fortunately this regime lasted only a few months.

During the whole of my commuting period I have always carried a brief case with both written and reading work so that the inevitable delays and hold-ups could be used to advantage. I have little sympathy for those who work themselves up to a near heart attack at every little hold up. Of course there have been many incidents and delays but, by and large, Anglia Railways has operated consistently well on its Intercity Norwich to London services. However, on one morning the early train broke down only a few yards beyond the tunnel at Ipswich and then, after about thirty minutes or so nothing had happened and with no announcement, some of the regulars pressed the guard who said that an engine was coming from Colchester to tow us into that station. After a further twenty minutes when nothing had happened the guard was again pressed to reveal the problem. With pleas not to let him down he divulged that Anglia were negotiating a contract with the Freight Company to borrow an engine. This at seven in the morning with few managers around. No wonder it was a slow process. When asked why the two could not have a standing contract we were told that it was not possible as no one knew where and when there might be a failure!! Anglia perform very well and I have many friends among the staff both now and over the whole period.

In Conclusion

I have been blessed with good health and with very good fortune during a long and exciting career including being involved in leading edge technology and in two 'world first' developments in radar, and in automatic landing, Friends and colleagues in the Royal Institute of Navigation, the Royal Aeronautical Society and the Federation of the Electronic Industries have, over the years, tried to persuade me to record my experiences in the interests of some important technological history which, to date, has received little or no general exposure.

Now, looking back at this rather disjointed effort I can but hope that it serves this purpose. However, to my surpise, I have enjoyed writing it since, as one gets older, in my experience the past seems to become more important than the future.

I am now anxious to thank all of those who have contributed so very much to an exciting and active career which has provided the background to this story. I am well aware that, in addition to those I have included in the formal acknowledgements and those mentioned in the text, there are many others who have contributed to an interesting and generally happy experience. I wish to say a very grateful 'thank you' to you all.

THE END

Appendix

Some 1.5mtr AIRBORNE RADAR STATISTICS

Note

1.5 mtr ASV was the first Airborne Radar equipment in production and became the basis upon which AI, Rebecca, Lucero and the Army and Navy adaptations were developed.

ASV (Air to Surface Vessel)

    Submarine Sinkings and Suppression

1941 to 1943	70 Sunk
1943	Effective Suppression

    Convoy Control and Protection

Starting in 1941	Increasing Loss Reduction

ASV Equipment Produced

1941 onwards	20,000 plus produced in the UK USA, Canada and Australia

Rebecca/Lucero/Eureka

1942 onwards	35,000 plus produced

AI (Air Interception)

    One AI Night-fighter equivalent to five aircraft
on a clear night and fifty in moderate cloud.
On a dark night or in full cloud without
AI interception was practically useless.

Army Operations

    Searchlight Guidance
Ack Ack Gun Aiming

Navy Operations

    Destroyers and Small Boats Search and Warning.
Swordfish and Walrus Aircraft Search and Homing.
Coast Protection-Low Level Cover all round the coast.